The Supporters Guide to Scottish Football 2000

EDITOR
John Robinson

Eighth Edition

British Library Cataloguing in Publication Data
A catalogue record for this book is available from the British Library

ISBN 1-86223-038-2

Printed by The Cromwell Press

FOREWORD

We wish to thank the club secretaries of the Scottish Premier League, the Scottish League, the Highland League and the East of Scotland League for their assistance in providing the information contained in this guide. We also wish to thank Bob Budd (cover artwork), Owen Pavey & Kevin Norminton (photos), David Thomson (Scottish Football League), J.H. Grant (Highland League) and J.M. Greenhorn (East of Scotland League) for their valuable assistance.

This year we have again provided new ground photos for many grounds, each reflecting the tremendous changes which are taking place.

When using this guide, readers should note that most clubs also extend the child concessionary prices to include Senior Citizens.

As part of our ongoing aim to improve our publications, readers are invited to let us know if they experience any difficulties with this guide, particularly incorrect directions, phone numbers or club information.

Regular readers will note that we have re-introduced the East of Scotland League Information this year and we are currently photographing the grounds from this League to further extend this in our next edition.

Finally, we would like to wish our readers a happy and safe spectating season.

John Robinson
EDITOR

CONTENTS

HAMPDEN –
SCOTLAND'S NATIONAL STADIUM

Opened: 1903
Location: Hampden Park, Mount Florida,
Glasgow G42 9BA
Telephone Nº: (0141) 640-4000
Fax Number: (0141) 636-6087

Record Attendance: 150,239
(Scotland vs England, 17th April 1937)
Pitch Size: 115 × 75 yards
Ground Capacity: 52,145 (All seats)

GENERAL INFORMATION

Car Parking: Car Park for 600 cars at
the Stadium
Coach Parking: Stadium Car Park
Nearest Railway Station: Mount
Florida and King's Park (both 5
minutes walk)
Nearest Bus Station: Buchanan Street
Nearest Police Station: Aikenhead
Road, Glasgow
Police Telephone Nº: (0141) 532-4900

DISABLED INFORMATION

Wheelchairs: Accommodated in disabled spectators sections
at all levels in the South Stand, particularly levels 1 and 4
where special catering and toilet facilities are available.
Disabled Toilets: Available
Commentaries are available for the blind + a CCTV link with
commentary for other disabled supporters
Contact: (0141) 620-4000

NORTH STAND

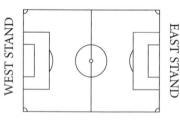

WEST STAND

EAST STAND

SOUTH STAND

Travelling Supporters' Information:
Routes: From the South: Take the A724 to the Cambuslang Road and at Eastfield branch left into Main Street
and follow through Burnhill Street and Westmuir Place into Prospecthill Road. Turn left into Aikenhead Road
and right into Mount Annan for Kinghorn Drive and the Stadium; From the South: Take the A77 Fenwick
Road, through Kilmarnock Road into Pollokshaws Road then turn right into Langside Avenue. Pass through
Battle Place to Battlefield Road and turn left into Cathcart Road. Turn right into Letherby Drive, right into
Carmunnock Road and 1st left into Mount Annan Drive for the Stadium; From the North & East: Exit M8
Junction 15 and passing Infirmary on left proceed into High Street and cross the Albert Bridge into Crown Street.
Join Cathcart Road and proceed South until it becomes Carmunnock Road. Turn left into Mount Annan Drive
and left again into Kinghorn Drive for the Stadium.

THE SCOTTISH
FOOTBALL ASSOCIATION

Founded
1873

Address
6 Park Gardens, Glasgow   G3 7YF

Phone
(0141) 332-6372

THE SCOTTISH
FOOTBALL LEAGUE

Founded
1890

Address
188 West Regent Street, Glasgow   G2 4RY

Phone
(0141) 248-3844

ABERDEEN FC

Founded: 1903 (**Entered League:** 1904)
Former Names: None
Nickname: 'The Dons'
Ground: Pittodrie Stadium, Pittodrie Street, Aberdeen AB24 5QH
Record Attendance: 45,061 (13/3/54)
Pitch Size: 109 × 71 yards

Colours: Shirts – Red
    Shorts – Red
Telephone Nº: (01224) 650400
Ticket Office: (01224) 632328
Fax Number: (01224) 644173
Ground Capacity: 22,199 (all seats)

MERKLAND STAND
FAMILY ENCLOSURE

SOUTH STAND

SOUTH STAND
EAST (Away)

(PITTODRIE STREET)
MAIN STAND

RICHARD DONALD STAND
GOLF ROAD

GENERAL INFORMATION

Supporters Club: Susan Scott, Aldon, Wellington Road, Aberdeen AB1 4BJ
Telephone Nº: (01224) 898260
Car Parking: Beach Boulevard, King Street & Golf Road
Coach Parking: Beach Boulevard
Nearest Railway Station: Aberdeen (1 mile)
Nearest Bus Station: Aberdeen
Club Shop: AFC Direct , Bridge Street, Aberdeen
Opening Times: 9.00am to 5.30pm
Telephone Nº: (01224) 405305
Postal Sales: Yes
Nearest Police Station: Aberdeen
Police Telephone Nº: (01224) 639111

GROUND INFORMATION

Away Supporters' Entrances & Sections:
Park Road entrance for the South Stand East

ADMISSION INFO (1999/2000 PRICES)

Adult Seating: £14.00 to £20.00
Child Seating: £8.00 to £20.00
Family Section: £8.00 per child in Family Section.
Programme Price: £1.50

DISABLED INFORMATION

Wheelchairs: 26 spaces available in front of the Richard Donald Stand & Merkland Stand
Helpers: One helper admitted per wheelchair
Prices: Free of charge for the disabled
Disabled Toilets: One available in Richard Donald Stand and one is available by the Merkland Stand
Are Bookings Necessary: Yes
Contact: (01224) 650423

Travelling Supporters' Information:
Routes: From the City Centre, travel along Union Street then turn left into King Street. The Stadium is about ½ mile along King Street (A92) on the right-hand side.

AIRDRIEONIANS FC

Founded: 1878 (**Entered League:** 1903)
Former Names: Excelsior FC
Nickname: 'Diamonds'
Ground: Shyberry Excelsior Stadium, Broomfield Park, Craigneuk Avenue, Airdrie ML6 8QZ
Record Attendance: –
Pitch Size: 115 × 75 yards

Colours: Shirts – White with Red Diamond
Shorts – Red
Telephone N°: (01236) 622000
Ticket Office: (01236) 747255
Fax Number: (01236) 626002
Ground Capacity: 10,156 (All seats)
Correspondence: G.W. Peat, 32 Stirling Street, Airdrie ML6 0AH

SOUTH STAND

EAST STAND

JACK DALZIEL STAND

NORTH STAND

GENERAL INFORMATION

Supporters Club: David Johnstone, 16 Deveron Street, Coatbridge
Telephone N°: (01236) 423812
Car Parking: Behind all the Stands
Coach Parking: Behind the East Stand
Nearest Railway Station: Airdrie (1½ miles)
Nearest Bus Station: Gartlea – Airdrie Town Centre
Club Shop: 93 Graham Street, Airdrie & at ground
Opening Times: Graham Street: Weekdays 9.00am to 5.00pm. Saturdays 9.00am to 4.00pm. Closed for lunch 12.30pm to 1.30pm. Ground: Opens 1 hour before matches
Telephone N°: (01236) 747255
Postal Sales: Yes
Nearest Police Station: Anderson Street, Airdrie
Police Telephone N°: (01236) 762222

GROUND INFORMATION

Away Supporters' Entrances & Sections:
East and South Stands

ADMISSION INFO (1999/2000 PRICES)

Adult Seating: £12.00
Child Seating: £7.00
One adult and one child: £16.00
Programme Price: £1.50

DISABLED INFORMATION

Wheelchairs: Spaces available for home and away fans accommodated in the front sections
Helpers: One admitted per disabled supporter
Prices: Free for the disabled. Helpers normal price
Disabled Toilets: Available in all the stands
Are Bookings Necessary: Preferable
Contact: (01236) 762067

Travelling Supporters' Information:
Routes: From the East: Exit the M8 at Junction 6 and take the A73 (signposted Cumbernauld). Pass through Chapelhall into Airdrie and turn right into Petersburn Road – the ground is on the left; From the West: Take the A8 to the Chapelhall turn-off for Chapelhall. Join the A73 at Chapelhall, then as above.

ALBION ROVERS FC

Founded: 1882 (**Entered League:** 1903)
Former Names: None
Nickname: 'Wee Rovers'
Ground: Cliftonhill Stadium, Main Street, Coatbridge, Lanarkshire   ML5 3RB
Record Attendance: 27,381 (8/2/36)
Pitch Size: 110 × 72 yards

Colours: Shirts – Yellow with Red Trim
  Shorts – Yellow
Telephone Nº: (01236) 606334
Ticket Office: (01236) 607041
Fax Number: (01236) 606334
Ground Capacity: 2,496
Seating Capacity: 538

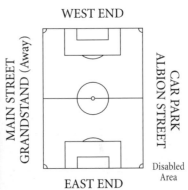

WEST END

MAIN STREET
GRANDSTAND (Away)

ALBION STREET

CAR PARK

Disabled Area

EAST END

GENERAL INFORMATION
Supporters Club: None
Telephone Nº: –
Car Parking: Street Parking and Albion Street
Coach Parking: Albion Street
Nearest Railway Station: Coatdyke (10 mins. walk)
Nearest Bus Station: Coatbridge
Club Shop: At ground
Opening Times: One hour before each home match
Telephone Nº: (01236) 606334
Postal Sales: Yes
Nearest Police Station: Coatbridge (½ mile)
Police Telephone Nº: (01236) 50200

GROUND INFORMATION
Away Supporters' Entrances & Sections:
Main Street entrance for the Main Street Area

ADMISSION INFO (1999/2000 PRICES)
Adult Standing: £6.00
Adult Seating: £7.00
Child Standing: £3.00
Child Seating: £4.00
Programme Price: £1.00

DISABLED INFORMATION
Wheelchairs: Approximately 30 spaces available in the Disabled Area
Helpers: Please phone the club for information
Prices: Please phone the club for information
Disabled Toilets: One available at the East End of the Ground
Are Bookings Necessary: No, but preferred
Contact: (01236) 606334

Travelling Supporters' Information:
Routes: From East or West: Take the A8/M8 to the Shawhead Interchange then follow the A725 to the Town Centre. Take A89 signs towards Airdrie at the roundabout, the ground is then on the left; From the South: Take the A725 from Bellshill/Hamilton/Motherwell/M74 to Coatbridge. Take A89 signs towards Airdrie at the roundabout, the ground is then on the left; From North: Take A73 to Airdrie then follow signs for A8010 to Coatbridge. Join the A89 and the ground is one mile on the right.

ALLOA ATHLETIC FC

Founded: 1878 (**Entered League:** 1921)
Former Names: None
Nickname: 'The Wasps'
Ground: Recreation Park, Clackmannan Road, Alloa FK10 1RY
Record Attendance: 13,000 (26/2/39)
Pitch Size: 110 × 75 yards

Colours: Shirts – Gold and Black
Shorts – Black
Telephone Nº: (01259) 722695
Ticket Office: (01259) 722695
Fax Number: (01259) 210886
Ground Capacity: 3,148
Seating Capacity: 424

CLACKMANNAN ROAD / HILTON ROAD / MAIN STAND

GENERAL INFORMATION

Supporters Club: R. Snaddon, c/o Club
Telephone Nº: (01259) 722695
Car Parking: A Car Park is adjacent to the Ground
Coach Parking: By Police Direction
Nearest Railway Station: Stirling (7 miles)
Nearest Bus Station: Alloa
Club Shop: At ground
Opening Times: Matchdays only 1.30pm to 5.00pm
Telephone Nº: (01259) 722695
Postal Sales: Yes
Nearest Police Station: Alloa (½ mile)
Police Telephone Nº: (01259) 723255

GROUND INFORMATION

Away Supporters' Entrances & Sections:
Hilton Road entrance for the Hilton Road Side and
Clackmannan Road End

ADMISSION INFO (1999/2000 PRICES)

Adult Standing: £8.00
Adult Seating: £9.00
Child Standing: £4.00
Child Seating: £5.00
Programme Price: £1.00

DISABLED INFORMATION

Wheelchairs: Accommodated in the Disabled Section underneath the Main Stand
Helpers: Admitted
Prices: Free of charge for the disabled and helpers
Disabled Toilets: One available in the Main Stand
Are Bookings Necessary: No
Contact: (01259) 722695

Travelling Supporters' Information:
Routes: From the South & East: Take the M74 to the M80 and exit at Junction 9 following the A907 into Alloa. Continue over two roundabouts passing the brewery and Town Centre. The Ground is on the left-hand side of the road.

ARBROATH FC

Founded: 1878 **(Entered League:** 1902)	**Colours:** Shirts – Maroon and White
Former Names: None	Shorts – Maroon with White trim
Nickname: 'The Red Lichties'	**Telephone Nº:** (01241) 872157
Ground: Gayfield Park, Arbroath	**Ticket Office:** (01241) 872157
DD11 1QB	**Fax Number:** (01241) 872157
Record Attendance: 13,510 (23/2/52)	**Ground Capacity:** 6,488
Pitch Size: 115 × 71 yards	**Seating Capacity:** 715

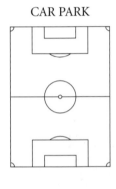

CAR PARK

QUEEN'S DRIVE DUNDEE ROAD

GENERAL INFORMATION

Supporters Club: Nicola Seldon, c/o Club
Telephone Nº: (01241) 439376
Car Parking: Car Park in Queen's Drive
Coach Parking: Car Park in Queen's Drive
Nearest Railway Station: Arbroath (15 mins. walk)
Nearest Bus Station: Arbroath (10 minutes walk)
Club Shop: Premier Sports, West Port, Arbroath
Opening Times: Monday-Saturday 9.00am-5.00pm
Telephone Nº: (01241) 872838
Postal Sales: Yes
Nearest Police Station: Arbroath
Police Telephone Nº: (01241) 872222

GROUND INFORMATION

Away Supporters' Entrances & Sections:
None specifically unless it is an all-ticket game, in
which case the Queen's Drive End is for Away fans

ADMISSION INFO (1999/2000 PRICES)

Adult Standing: £8.00
Adult Seating: £9.00
Child Standing: £4.00
Child Seating: £5.00
Programme Price: £1.00

DISABLED INFORMATION

Wheelchairs: 10 spaces available at the West End of
the Main Stand
Helpers: Admitted
Prices: Normal prices for the disabled and helpers
Disabled Toilets: One available by the Club Shop
Are Bookings Necessary: Yes
Contact: (01241) 872157

Travelling Supporters' Information:
Routes: From Dundee and the West: Take the A92 (Coast Road). On entering Arbroath, pass under the Railway
Line and the ground is on the right-hand side; From Stonehaven/Montrose: Take the A92, pass through Arbroath
and past the Harbour and the ground is on the left-hand side.

AYR UNITED FC

Founded: 1910 (**Entered League:** 1910)
Former Names: Ayr Parkhouse FC
& Ayr FC (amalgamated in 1910)
Nickname: 'The Honest Men'
Ground: Somerset Park, Tryfield Place,
Ayr KA8 9NB
Record Attendance: 25,225 (13/9/69)
Pitch Size: 110 × 72 yards

Colours: Shirts – White
Shorts – Black
Telephone Nº: (01292) 263435/263436
Ticket Office: (01292) 263435/263436
Fax Number: (01292) 281314
Ground Capacity: 12,178
Seating Capacity: 1,500

RAILWAY END (Away)

MAIN STAND / TRYFIELD PLACE

FAMILY STAND (DISABLED)

(Away) | HOME TERRACE

SOMERSET ROAD

GENERAL INFORMATION
Supporters Club: c/o Club
Telephone Nº: (01292) 263435
Car Parking: Craigie Car Park, Ayr Racecourse and Somerset Road Car Park
Coach Parking: Craigie Car Park
Nearest Railway Station: Ayr or Newton-on-Ayr (both stations are 10 minutes walk)
Nearest Bus Station: Sandgate, Ayr
Club Shop: At the Ground
Opening Times: Weekdays 8.30am to 5.30pm
Home matchdays 11.00am to 3.00pm
Telephone Nº: (01292) 263435/263436
Postal Sales: Yes
Nearest Police Station: King Street, Ayr (½ mile)
Police Telephone Nº: (01292) 664000

GROUND INFORMATION
Away Supporters' Entrances & Sections:
Turnstiles 1-7 for the Railway End (covered terrace)

+ turnstiles 9-10 for Main Stand accommodation

ADMISSION INFO (1999/2000 PRICES)
Adult Standing: £10.00
Adult Seating: £13.00
Child/Senior Citizen Standing: £5.00
Child Seating: In the Family Stand only – 1 Adult + 1 Child for £12.00 (each additional child is £5.00)
Programme Price: £1.50

DISABLED INFORMATION
Wheelchairs: 24 spaces are available in the Disabled Area beneath the Family Stand
Helpers: One admitted per wheelchair
Prices: Free for one wheelchair plus helper
Disabled Toilets: 2 Gents and 1 Ladies available in the Disabled Area
Are Bookings Necessary: Only for all-ticket games
Contact: (01292) 263435/263436

Travelling Supporters' Information:
Routes: Make for A77 Ring Road around Ayr, exit via Whitletts Roundabout onto the A719 and follow road towards Ayr. Just past the end of the racecourse, turn right at traffic lights into Burnett Terrace, sharp left and right takes you into Somerset Road. (For car parking on Matchdays turn left at traffic lights and then right 50 yards on into Craigie Park or on Somerset Road just past the ground on the left into Somerset Road car park).

BERWICK RANGERS FC

Founded: 1881 (**Entered League:** 1951)
Former Names: None
Nickname: 'The Borderers'
Ground: Shielfield Park, Shielfield Terrace,
Tweedmouth, Berwick-upon-Tweed TD15 2EF
Record Attendance: 13,365 (28/1/67)
Pitch Size: 110 × 70 yards

Colours: Shirts – Black and Gold Stripes
Shorts – Black
Telephone Nº: (01289) 307424
Ticket Office: (01289) 307424
Fax Number: (01289) 307424
Ground Capacity: 4,131
Seating Capacity: 1,366

SHIELFIELD TERRACE

POPULAR SIDE TERRACING (Away)

MAIN STAND (All Seats) (CAR PARK)

GENERAL INFORMATION

Supporters Club: Gordon Dickson, 19 Greenwood, Tweedmouth, Berwick-upon-Tweed
Telephone Nº: (01289) 308317
Car Parking: Large Car Park at the Ground
Coach Parking: Car Park at the Ground
Nearest Railway Station: Berwick-upon-Tweed (1½ miles)
Nearest Bus Station: Berwick Town Centre (1 mile)
Club Shop: At the Supporters' Club in the Ground
Opening Times: Matchdays Only
Telephone Nº: (01289) 307424
Postal Sales: Yes – via Supporters' Club at Ground
Nearest Police Station: Church Street (1 mile)
Police Telephone Nº: (01289) 307111

GROUND INFORMATION

Away Supporters' Entrances & Sections:
Shielfield Terrace entrance for Popular Side Terrace

ADMISSION INFO (1999/2000 PRICES)

Adult Standing: £7.00
Adult Seating: £7.00
Concessions: £3.00
Programme Price: £1.00

DISABLED INFORMATION

Wheelchairs: Accommodated in the Main Stand
Helpers: Admitted with wheelchair disabled
Prices: Concessionary prices apply to the disabled
Disabled Toilets: Available in the General Toilet Block and also in the Club Offices
Are Bookings Necessary: Yes
Contact: (01289) 307424 or 307623

Travelling Supporters' Information:
Routes: From the North: Take the A1 (Berwick Bypass), cross new road-bridge then at roundabout take 1st exit. Carry on for approximately ¼ mile to the next roundabout, go straight across then continue approximately ¼ mile into Shielfield Terrace. Turn left and the ground is on the left; From South: Take A1 Bypass and continue across the first roundabout towards Scremerston/Tweedmouth and then on for 1 mile. At the crossroads/junction take 'Spittal' Road (right) and continue for approximately 1 mile until the road becomes Shielfield Terrace. The ground is on the left.

BRECHIN CITY FC

Founded: 1906 (**Entered League:** 1923)
Former Names: None
Nickname: 'The City'
Ground: Glebe Park, Trinity Road,
Brechin, Angus   DD9 6BJ
Record Attendance: 8,244 (3/2/73)
Pitch Size: 110 × 76 yards

Colours: Shirts – Red and White
      Shorts – Red and White
Telephone Nº: (01356) 622856
Ticket Office: (01356) 622856
Fax Number: (01356) 625667
Secretary's Number: (01356) 625691
Ground Capacity: 3,900
Seating Capacity: 1,518

COVERED TERRACING

TERRACING

STAND

TRINITY ROAD
SEATED ENCLOSURE

GENERAL INFORMATION

Supporters Club: c/o Glebe Park
Telephone Nº: (01356) 622856
Car Parking: Small Car Park at the Ground and
Street Parking
Coach Parking: Street Parking
Nearest Railway Station: Montrose (8 miles)
Nearest Bus Station: Brechin
Club Shop: At ground
Opening Times: Matchdays Only
Telephone Nº: (01356) 622856
Postal Sales: Yes
Nearest Police Station: Brechin (400 yards)
Police Telephone Nº: (01356) 622222

GROUND INFORMATION

Away Supporters' Entrances & Sections:
No segregation usually

ADMISSION INFO (1999/2000 PRICES)

Adult Standing: £5.00
Adult Seating: £5.00
Child Standing: £2.50
Child Seating: £2.50
Programme Price: £1.00

DISABLED INFORMATION

Wheelchairs: 10 spaces each available for home and
away fans
Helpers: Please phone the club for details
Prices: Please phone the club for details
Disabled Toilets: 2 available in Covered Enclosure
Are Bookings Necessary: Yes
Contact: (01356) 622856

Travelling Supporters' Information:
Routes: From the South and West: Take the M90 to the A94 and continue along past the first 'Brechin' turn-off.
Take the second turn signposted 'Brechin'. On entering Brechin, the ground is on the left-hand side of the road
between some houses.

CELTIC FC

Founded: 1888 (**Entered League:** 1890)	**Colours:** Shirts – Green & White Hoops
Former Names: None	Shorts – White
Nickname: 'The Bhoys' 'The Hoops'	**Telephone Nº:** (0141) 556-2611
Ground: Celtic Park, Glasgow, G40 3RE	**Ticket Office:** (0141) 551-8653
Record Attendance: 92,000 (1/1/38)	**Fax Number:** (0141) 551-8106
Pitch Size: 115 × 74 yards	**Ground Capacity:** 60,506 (All seats)

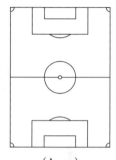

WEST STAND

LONDON ROAD SOUTH STAND

(JANEFIELD STREET) NORTH STAND

(Away)
EAST STAND

GENERAL INFORMATION

Supporters Club: Celtic Supporters' Association, Barrowfield Ground, 1524 London Road, Glasgow, G40 3RJ
Telephone Nº: (0141) 556-1882
Car Parking: Limited on Matchdays to those with a Valid Car Park Pass. Otherwise, street parking
Coach Parking: Gallowgate, Fielden Street, Biggar Street and Nuneaton Street
Nearest Railway Station: Bellgrove (10 mins. walk)
Nearest Bus Stop: Outside of the ground
Club Shop: Superstore at Celtic Park. Celtic shops also at Level 1 of North Stand; 21 High Street, Glasgow; 40 Dundas Street, Glasgow; Level 1, Jervis Centre, Dublin
Opening Times: Superstore: Mon-Sat 9am-6pm. Sundays 10am-5pm; North Stand: 2 hours before kick-off & half-time; High Street: Mon-Sat 9.30-5.30. Sun. 11.30-4.30; Dundas Street: Mon-Sat 9-5; Dublin Shop: Mon-Sat at least 9.30-6.00 (later on some days). Also open Sundays 12.00pm–6.00pm
Telephone Nº: (0141) 554-4231 (Superstore)
Mail-Order Sales: Yes – (0141) 550-1888

Nearest Police Station: London Road (½ mile)
Police Telephone Nº: (0141) 532-4600

GROUND INFORMATION

Away Supporters' Entrances & Sections:
Kinloch Street Turnstiles for the East Stand

ADMISSION INFO (1999/2000 PRICES)

Adult Seating: £16.00 – £23.00
Child Seating: £8.00 when accompanied by adult in certain sections of the ground
Programme Price: £1.50

DISABLED INFORMATION

Wheelchairs: 136 spaces for home fans and 6 spaces for away fans in the North Stand and East Stand
Helpers: 90 helpers admitted home fans, 6 for away
Prices: £8.00 – subject to availability (waiting list). This covers a disabled fan and a helper
Disabled Toilets: 5 available in the North Stand, 2 in the East Stand and 3 in the South West Stand
Contact: (0141) 551-4311 (bookings are necessary)

Travelling Supporters' Information:
Routes: From the South and East: Take the A74 London Road towards the City Centre, Celtic Park is on the right about ½ mile past the Belvidere Hospital and the ground is clearly visible; From the West: Take the A74 London Road from the City Centre and turn left about ½ mile past Bridgeton Station.

18

CLYDE FC

Founded: 1878 (**Entered League:** 1906)
Former Names: None
Nickname: 'Bully Wee'
Ground: Broadwood Stadium,
Cumbenauld, Glasgow G68 9NE
Record Attendance: 8,000 (14/8/96)
Pitch Size: 115 × 75 yards

Colours: Shirts – White + Red & Black
 Shorts – Black
Telephone Nº: (01236) 451511
Ticket Office: (01236) 451511
Fax Number: (01236) 733490
Ground Capacity: 8,200 (all seats)

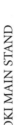

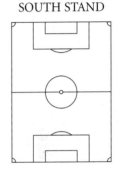

SOUTH STAND

OKI MAIN STAND

WEST STAND

GENERAL INFORMATION

Supporters Club: None
Telephone Nº: –
Car Parking: Behind the Main and West Stands
Coach Parking: Behind the Main Stand
Nearest Railway Station: Croy (1½ miles)
Nearest Bus Station: Cumbernauld Town Centre
Club Shop: At ground
Opening Times: One hour before a match and after
the match
Telephone Nº: (01236) 451511
Postal Sales: Yes
Nearest Police Station: South Muirhead Street,
Cumbernauld
Police Telephone Nº: (01236) 736085

GROUND INFORMATION

Away Supporters' Entrances & Sections:
West Stand Turnstile for the West Stand area

ADMISSION INFO (1999/2000 PRICES)

Adult Seating: £9.00
Child Seating: £1.00
Programme Price: £1.50

DISABLED INFORMATION

Wheelchairs: 10 spaces each for home and away
fans accommodated in front sections of each stand
Helpers: One helper admitted per wheelchair
Prices: Free of charge for the disabled
Disabled Toilets: 4 available in Main & West Stands
Are Bookings Necessary: No
Contact: (01236) 451511

Travelling Supporters' Information:
Routes: From all Parts: Exit the A80 at Broadwood Junction and follow the signs for Broadwood. The Ground is
signposted from the next roundabout.

CLYDEBANK FC

Founded: 1965 (**Entered League:** 1966)	**Pitch Size:** 110 × 71 yards
Former Names: None	**Colours:** Shirts – Red and White Stripes
Nickname: 'The Bankies'	Shorts – Black
Ground: Cappielow Park, Sinclair Street,	**Telephone Nº:** (0141) 955-9048
Greenock PA15 2TY	**Ticket Office:** (0141) 955-9048
Office Address: c/o West of Scotland RFC,	**Fax Number:** (0141) 955-9049
Burnbrae, Milngavie, Glasgow G62 6HX	**Ground Capacity:** 14,267
Record Attendance: 18,000 (2/3/57)	**Seating Capacity:** 5,257

SINCLAIR STREET

EAST HAMILTON TERRACE
(DUBLIN END)

Clydebank are groundsharing with Greenock Morton during 1999/2000

GENERAL INFORMATION
Supporters Club: c/o Club
Telephone Nº: –
Car Parking: At the ground
Coach Parking: James Watt Dock
Nearest Railway Station: Cartsdyke (½ mile)
Nearest Bus Station: Town Centre (1½ miles)
Club Shop: c/o Office Address
Opening Times: Office Hours
Telephone Nº: (0141) 955-9048
Postal Sales: Yes
Nearest Police Station: Rue End Street, Greenock
Police Telephone Nº: (01475) 724444

GROUND INFORMATION
Away Supporters' Entrances & Sections:
East Hamilton Street turnstiles

ADMISSION INFO (1999/2000 PRICES)
Adult Standing: £8.00
Adult Seating: £10.00
Child Standing: £4.00
Child Seating: £6.00
Programme Price: £1.00

DISABLED INFORMATION
Wheelchairs: 5 spaces each for home and away fans accommodated below the Grandstand
Helpers: Please phone the club for information
Prices: Please phone the club for information
Disabled Toilets: None
Are Bookings Necessary: Yes
Contact: (01475) 723571

Travelling Supporters' Information:
Routes: From All Parts: Take the M8 to the A8. Pass through Port Glasgow and turn left after passing the dockyard buildings on the right-hand side of the road.

COWDENBEATH FC

Founded: 1881 (**Entered League:** 1921)
Former Names: The Miners FC
Nickname: 'Cowden' or 'Blue Brazil'
Ground: Central Park, High Street,
Cowdenbeath   KY4 9EY
Record Attendance: 25,586 (21/4/49)
Pitch Size: 107 × 64 yards

Colours: Shirts – Royal blue + white band
    Shorts – White with blue side panel
Telephone Nº: (01383) 610166
Ticket Office: (01383) 610166
Fax Number: (01383) 512132
Ground Capacity: 4,370
Seating Capacity: 1,431

MAIN STREET
(EAST TERRACING)

(NORTH SIDE)
GRANDSTAND

(Away)   SOUTH SIDE

WEST TERRACING

GENERAL INFORMATION

Supporters Club: W. Nellies, c/o Club
Telephone Nº: (01383) 610166
Car Parking: Car Park at the ground and Stenhouse
Street (200 yards). A total of 200 spaces are available
Coach Parking: King Street and Rowan Terrace
Nearest Railway Station: Cowdenbeath (400 yards)
Nearest Bus Station: Cowdenbeath (Bus Stop at the
ground)
Club Shop: At ground
Opening Times: Weekdays 10.00am to 3.00pm;
Saturdays 1.00pm to 3.00pm
Telephone Nº: (01383) 610166
Postal Sales: Yes
Nearest Police Station: Cowdenbeath (300 yards)
Police Telephone Nº: (01383) 318600

GROUND INFORMATION

Away Supporters' Entrances & Sections:
Main Entrance for the South and East Sides

ADMISSION INFO (1999/2000 PRICES)

Adult Standing: £7.00
Adult Seating: £8.00
Child Standing: £3.00
Child Seating: £3.50
Programme Price: 80p

DISABLED INFORMATION

Wheelchairs: 3 spaces each for home and away fans
Helpers: Please phone the club for information
Prices: Please phone the club for information
Disabled Toilets: 1 Ladies, 1 Gents and 1 Unisex
available
Are Bookings Necessary: Yes
Contact: (01383) 610166

Travelling Supporters' Information:
Routes: Exit the M90 at Junction 3 for Dunfermline. Take the Dual Carriageway to Cowdenbeath and follow
straight on into the High Street. The ground is situated on the first left turn in the High Street.

DUMBARTON FC

Founded: 1872 (**Entered League:** 1890)
Former Names: None
Nickname: 'Sons'
Ground: Boghead Park, Miller Street, Dumbarton G82 2JA
Record Attendance: 18,000 (2/3/57)
Pitch Size: 110 × 68 yards

Colours: Shirts – Gold with Black Trim
Shorts – Black
Telephone Nº: (01389) 762569
Ticket Office: (01389) 762569
Fax Number: (01389) 762629
Ground Capacity: 4,500
Seating Capacity: 303

(OVERWOOD DRIVE)
COVERED ENCLOSURE

MILLER STREET MAIN STAND

EAST TERRACE

(Away)
COVERED ENCLOSURE
(BOGHEAD AVENUE)

GENERAL INFORMATION
Supporters Club: c/o Club
Telephone Nº: –
Car Parking: Street Parking
Coach Parking: Dumbarton Common
Nearest Railway Station: Dumbarton (East) – (10 minute walk)
Nearest Bus Station: Dumbarton
Club Shop: At ground
Opening Times: Matchdays and Weekdays 10.00am to 1.00pm
Telephone Nº: (01389) 762569
Postal Sales: Yes
Nearest Police Station: Dumbarton
Police Telephone Nº: (01389) 763311

GROUND INFORMATION
Away Supporters' Entrances & Sections:
Boghead Avenue entrances for Covered Enclosure

ADMISSION INFO (1999/2000 PRICES)
Adult Standing: £7.00
Adult Seating: £10.00
Child Standing: £3.50
Child Seating: £6.00
Programme Price: £1.00

DISABLED INFORMATION
Wheelchairs: 3 trackside spaces for home fans only
Helpers: Please phone the club for information
Prices: Please phone the club for information
Disabled Toilets: One available in the Main Stand
Are Bookings Necessary: Yes
Contact: (01389) 762569

Dumbarton FC will be moving to a new ground near Dumbarton Castle in 2000.

Travelling Supporters' Information:
Routes: From All Parts: Exit M8 at Junction 17 and take A82 to Dumbarton. Follow signs for 'Loch Lomond' along dual carriageway and take left turn before B.P. Garage at traffic lights. Home entrance is then 2nd on left. Away supporters take left turn at Dunbritton Road (before B.P. Garage) and follow signs to Silverton area. Then walk to Boghead Avenue turnstiles.

DUNDEE FC

Founded: 1893 (**Entered League:** 1893) **Former Names:** None **Nickname:** 'The Dark Blues' **Ground:** Dens Park Stadium, Sandeman Street, Dundee DD3 7JY **Record Attendance:** 43,024 (7/2/53) **Pitch Size:** 105 × 68 yards	**Colours:** Shirts – Blue Shorts – White **Telephone Nº:** (01382) 889966 **Ticket Office:** (01382) 204777 **Fax Number:** (01382) 832284 **Ground Capacity:** 12,054 (All seats)

GENERAL INFORMATION

Supporters Club: Dave Forbes, c/o Club
Telephone Nº: (01382) 889966
Car Parking: Private 600 space Car Park available
Coach Parking: 50 yards from the ground
Nearest Railway Station: Dundee
Nearest Bus Station: Dundee
Club Shop: Commercial Street, Dundee
Opening Times: Weekdays 9.00am to 5.30pm
Telephone Nº: (01382) 205664
Postal Sales: Yes
Nearest Police Station: Bell Street, Dundee
Police Telephone Nº: (01382) 223200

GROUND INFORMATION

Away Supporters' Entrances & Sections:
Turnstiles 33-38 for East Stand and turnstiles 31-32 for Sections A, B & C of the Main Stand

ADMISSION INFO (1999/2000 PRICES)

Adult Seating: £13.00 – £15.00
Child Seating: £5.00 – £7.00
1 Adult + 1 Child: £15.00 in the Family Section
Programme Price: £1.50

DISABLED INFORMATION

Wheelchairs: Accommodated in the East and West Stands
Helpers: Admitted
Prices: Free for the disabled. Helpers £13.00
Disabled Toilets: Adjacent to the Disabled Area
Are Bookings Necessary: Yes
Contact: (01382) 826104

Travelling Supporters' Information:
Routes: Take the A972 from Perth (Kingsway West) to King's Cross Circus Roundabout. Take the 3rd exit into Clepington Road and turn right into Provost Road for 1 mile then take the 2nd left into Sandeman Street for the ground.

DUNDEE UNITED FC

Founded: 1909 (**Entered League:** 1910)
Former Names: Dundee Hibernians FC
Nickname: 'The Terrors'
Ground: Tannadice Park, Tannadice
Street, Dundee   DD3 7JW
Record Attendance: 28,000 (Nov. 1996)
Pitch Size: 110 × 72 yards

Colours: Shirts – Tangerine
                Shorts – Black
Telephone Nº: (01382) 833166
Ticket Office: (01382) 833166
Fax Number: (01382) 889398
Ground Capacity: 14,209 (all seats)

WEST STAND

FAIR PLAY STAND
(TANNADICE STREET)
SOUTH STAND

GEORGE FOX STAND

EAST STAND
ARKLAY STREET

GENERAL INFORMATION

Supporters Club: Andrew Woodrow, 3 Stevenson
Avenue, Glenrothes   KY6 1EE
Telephone Nº: (01592) 752129
Car Parking: Street Parking and Melrose Car Park
Coach Parking: Gussie Park (100 yards) and Dens Field
Nearest Railway Station: Dundee (20 mins. walk)
Nearest Bus Station: Dundee
Club Shop: At ground on Matchdays only or at
5 Victoria Road, Dundee
Opening Times: At ground: Matchdays 2.00pm to
5.00pm; Victoria Road: 9.00am to 5.30pm
Telephone Nº: (01382) 833166
Postal Sales: Yes
Nearest Police Station: Bell Street, Dundee
Police Telephone Nº: (01382) 223200

GROUND INFORMATION

Away Supporters' Entrances & Sections:
Turnsiles 7-16 for South Stand & Fair Play Stand

ADMISSION INFO (1999/2000 PRICES)

Adult Seating: £13.00 – £17.00
Child Seating: £8.00 – £10.00
Note: No concessions available on certain games
Programme Price: £1.50

DISABLED INFORMATION

Wheelchairs: Accommodated in the George Fox
Stand and the East and West Stands
Helpers: Please phone the club for details
Prices: Please phone the club for details
Disabled Toilets: Available in the George Fox Stand
and in the East and West Stands
Are Bookings Necessary: Yes
Contact: (01382) 833166

Travelling Supporters' Information:
Routes: From the South or West: Travel via Perth and take the A90 to Dundee. Once in Dundee join the Kingsway
(ring road) and follow this road until the third roundabout then turn right onto Old Glamis Road. Follow the
road to join Provost Road then turn left into Sandeman Street for the ground; From the North: Follow the A90
from Aberdeen and join the Kingsway (ring road). At the first set of traffic lights turn right into Clepington Road
and follow into Arklay Street before turning left into Tannadice Street for the ground.

DUNFERMLINE ATHLETIC FC

Founded: 1885 (**Entered League**: 1921)
Former Names: None
Nickname: 'The Pars'
Ground: East End Park, Halbeath Road,
Dunfermline, Fife   KY12 7RB
Record Attendance: 27,816 (30/4/68)
Pitch Size: 115 × 70 yards

Colours: Shirts – Black & White Stripes
Shorts – Black
Telephone Nº: (01383) 724295
Ticket Office: (01383) 724295
Fax Number: (01383) 723468
Ground Capacity: 12,565 (All seats)

GENERAL INFORMATION

Supporters Club: Mrs. J. Malcolm, 15 Meadowfield, Cowdenbeath
Telephone Nº: (01383) 611793
Car Parking: Multistorey Car Park is 10 mins. walk
Coach Parking: Leys Park Road
Nearest Railway Station: Dunfermline (15 minutes walk)
Nearest Bus Station: Carnegie Drive, Dunfermline (10 minutes walk)
Club Shop: Intersport, Kingsgate, Dunfermline
Opening Times: Monday-Saturday 9.00am-5.00pm
Telephone Nº: (01383) 739980
Postal Sales: Yes
Nearest Police Station: Holyrood Place (10 minutes walk)
Police Telephone Nº: (01383) 726711

GROUND INFORMATION

Away Supporters' Entrances & Sections:
Turnstiles 10-15 for the East Stand. Turnstiles 16-18 for the North East Stand

ADMISSION INFO (1999/2000 PRICES)

Adult Seating: £11.00 – £12.00
Child Seating: £5.00 – £6.00
Programme Price: £1.50

DISABLED INFORMATION

Wheelchairs: 12 spaces each for home & away fans
Helpers: One admitted per wheelchair
Prices: Free of charge for each wheelchair disabled and helper
Disabled Toilets: Available in the West and East Stands
Are Bookings Necessary: Yes
Contact: (01383) 724295

Travelling Supporters' Information:
Routes: From the Forth Road Bridge and Perth: Exit the M90 at Junction 3 and take A907 (Halbeath Road) into Dunfermline – Ground on right; From Kincardine Bridge and Alloa: Take A985 to A994 then into Dunfermline. Take Pittencrief Street, Glen Bridge and Carnegie Drive to Sinclair Gardens roundabout. Take 2nd exit into Appin Crescent and continue into Halbeath Road. Ground on left.

EAST FIFE FC

Founded: 1903 (**Entered League:** 1903)
Former Names: None
Nickname: 'The Fifers'
Ground: Bayview Stadium, Harbour
View, Methil, Fife   KY8 3RW
Record Attendance: 22,515 (2/1/50)
Pitch Size: 115 × 74 yards

Colours: Shirts – Amber & Black Diamonds
Shorts – Black + Amber Stripes
Telephone Nº: (01333) 426323
Ticket Office: (01333) 426323
Fax Number: (01333) 426376
Ground Capacity: 2,000 (All seats)

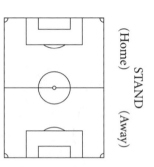

GENERAL INFORMATION
Supporters Club: Levenmouth Social Club
Telephone Nº: (01592) 757249
Car Parking: Adjacent to the ground
Coach Parking: Adjacent to the ground
Nearest Railway Station: Kirkcaldy (8 miles)
Nearest Bus Station: Leven
Club Shop: At ground
Opening Times: Matchdays + normal office hours
Telephone Nº: (01333) 426323
Postal Sales: Yes
Nearest Police Station: Sea Road, Methil (1 mile)
Police Telephone Nº: (01592) 418900

GROUND INFORMATION
Away Supporters' Entrances & Sections:
Accommodated within the Main Stand

ADMISSION INFO (1999/2000 PRICES)
Adult Seating: £8.50
Child Seating: £4.00
Programme Price: £1.00

DISABLED INFORMATION
Wheelchairs: 24 spaces available in total
Helpers: Admitted
Prices: Normal prices charged
Disabled Toilets: Yes
Are Bookings Necessary: Yes
Contact: (01333) 426323

Travelling Supporters' Information:
Routes: Take the A915 from Kirkcaldy past Buckhaven and Methil to Leven. Turn right at traffic lights and go straight on at the first roundabout then turn right at the second roundabout. Cross Bawbee Bridge and turn left at the next roundabout. The ground is the first turning on the left after ¼ mile.

EAST STIRLINGSHIRE FC

Founded: 1881 **(Entered League:** 1900)
Former Names: Bainsford Britannia FC
Nickname: 'The Shire'
Ground: Firs Park, Firs Street, Falkirk
FK2 7AY
Record Attendance: 12,000 (21/2/21)
Pitch Size: 112 × 72 yards

Colours: Shirts – Black & White Hoops
Shorts – Black
Telephone Nº: (01324) 623583
Ticket Office: (01324) 623583
Fax Number: (01324) 637862
Ground Capacity: 780
Seating Capacity: 280

WALLACE STREET
STAND
VICTORIA ROAD

GENERAL INFORMATION

Supporters Club: None
Telephone Nº: –
Car Parking: Street Parking
Coach Parking: Street Parking
Nearest Railway Station: Grahamston (10 minutes walk)
Nearest Bus Station: Falkirk
Club Shop: At ground
Opening Times: Weekdays (except Thursdays) and Saturday Matchdays 10.00am to 2.30pm
Telephone Nº: (01324) 623583
Postal Sales: Yes
Nearest Police Station: Falkirk (½ mile)
Police Telephone Nº: (01324) 634212

GROUND INFORMATION

Away Supporters' Entrances & Sections:
No usual segregation

ADMISSION INFO (1999/2000 PRICES)

Adult Standing: £6.00
Adult Seating: £7.00
OAP and Child Standing: £3.00
OAP and Child Seating: £3.00
Programme Price: £1.00

DISABLED INFORMATION

Wheelchairs: Accommodated
Helpers: Admitted
Prices: £3.00 each for both disabled and helpers
Disabled Toilets: Available in the Main Stand
Are Bookings Necessary: Yes
Contact: (01324) 623583

Travelling Supporters' Information:
Routes: From Glasgow and Edinburgh: Exit the Motorway at signs marked Grangemouth. Follow the AA signs for football traffic into Falkirk as far as Thornhill Road (where the road meets the 'Give Way' sign). Once in Thornhill Road turn left into Firs Street at St. James' Church. The Ground is straight ahead.

FALKIRK FC

<table>
<tr><td>

Founded: 1876 **(Entered League:** 1902)
Former Names: None
Nickname: 'The Bairns'
Ground: Brockville Park, Hope Street,
Falkirk   FK1 5AX
Record Attendance: 23,100 (21/2/53)
Pitch Size: 110 × 70 yards

</td><td>

Colours: Shirts – Navy Blue
            Shorts – White
Telephone Nº: (01324) 624121
Ticket Office: (01324) 624121
Fax Number: (01324) 612418
Ground Capacity: 7,576
Seating Capacity: 1,700

</td></tr>
</table>

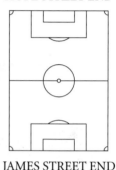

HOPE STREET END

COVERED ENCLOSURE
DISABLED ENCLOSURE

STAND   CAR PARK

JAMES STREET END

GENERAL INFORMATION

Supporters Club: Gordon McFarlane,
1 Summerford Gardens, Falkirk
Telephone Nº: (01324) 638104
Car Parking: Car Park at ground (200 spaces) and
also Town Car Park
Coach Parking: Town Car Park (100 yards)
Nearest Railway Station: Grahamston (100 yards)
Nearest Bus Station: Falkirk Centre (800 yards)
Club Shop: Glebe Street, Falkirk
Opening Times: 9.00am to 5.00pm
Telephone Nº: (01324) 639366
Postal Sales: Yes
Nearest Police Station: Hope Street, Falkirk (½ mile)
Police Telephone Nº: (01324) 634212

GROUND INFORMATION

Away Supporters' Entrances & Sections:
James Street entrances for the James Street End

ADMISSION INFO (1999/2000 PRICES)

Adult Standing: £10.00 – £11.50
Adult Seating: £13.50 – £15.00
Child Standing: £5.00 (£2.00 for Under-11's)
Child Seating: £6.50
Programme Price: £1.00

DISABLED INFORMATION

Wheelchairs: 14 spaces by the Watson Street Side
Helpers: Admitted
Prices: Normal prices charged
Disabled Toilets: Yes
Are Bookings Necessary: Yes
Contact: (01324) 624121

Travelling Supporters' Information:
Routes: From North and West: Exit M876 Junction 1 and take A883 into A803 to Falkirk. Pass along Camelon Road and West Bridge Street and turn left into Hope Street by Police Station. Follow along over railway line for Ground (about half a mile); From South & East: Take A803 road from Linlithglow into Falkirk along Callendar Road. Pass Callendar Shopping Centre (on right) along High Street and turn right into Hope Street by the Drookit & Duck pub (then as North & West).

FORFAR ATHLETIC FC

Founded: 1885 (**Entered League:** 1921)
Former Names: None
Nickname: 'Loons'
Ground: Station Park, Carseview Road, Forfar, Tayside
Record Attendance: 10,780 (2/2/70)
Pitch Size: 115 × 69 yards

Colours: Shirts – Sky Blue + Navy Trim
    Shorts – Navy Blue
Telephone Nº: (01307) 463576
Ticket Office: (01307) 463576
Fax Number: (01307) 466956
Ground Capacity: 8,388
Seating Capacity: 739

WEST END TERRACING
(Away)

SOUTH TERRACING (COVERED)

NORTH – MAIN STAND

EAST TERRACING

GENERAL INFORMATION

Supporters Club: Mrs. Y. Nicoll, 24 Turfbeg Drive, Forfar DD8 3LH
Telephone Nº: (01307) 467255
Car Parking: Market Muir Car Park and adjacent streets
Coach Parking: Mark Muir Car Park
Nearest Railway Station: Dundee or Arbroath (both 14 miles)
Nearest Bus Station: Forfar (½ mile)
Club Shop: None
Opening Times: –
Telephone Nº: –
Postal Sales: Yes
Nearest Police Station: West High Street, Forfar
Police Telephone Nº: (01307) 462551

GROUND INFORMATION

Away Supporters' Entrances & Sections:
West End entrances for West End Terracing and North part of the Main Stand

ADMISSION INFO (1999/2000 PRICES)

Adult Standing: £7.00
Adult Seating: £7.50
Child Standing: £3.00
Child Seating: £3.50
Programme Price: £1.00

DISABLED INFORMATION

Wheelchairs: 4 spaces each for home and away fans accommodated to the west of the Main Stand
Helpers: Please phone the club for details
Prices: Please phone the club for details
Disabled Toilets: One available
Are Bookings Necessary: Yes
Contact: (01307) 463576

Travelling Supporters' Information:
Routes: Take A85/M90 to Dundee and then the A929. Exit at the 2nd turn-off (signposted Forfar). On the outskirts of Forfar, turn right at the T-junction and then left at the next major road. The ground is signposted on the left (cobbled street with railway arch).

GREENOCK MORTON FC

Founded: 1874 (**Entered League:** 1893)	**Colours:** Shirts – Blue and White Hoops
Former Names: None	Shorts – White
Nickname: 'Ton'	**Telephone Nº:** (01475) 723571
Ground: Cappielow Park, Sinclair Street,	**Ticket Office:** (01475) 723571
Greenock PA15 2TY	**Fax Number:** (01475) 781084
Record Attendance: 23,500 (29/4/21)	**Ground Capacity:** 14,267
Pitch Size: 110 × 71 yards	**Seating Capacity:** 5,257

SINCLAIR STREET

COWSHED   GRANDSTAND

EAST HAMILTON TERRACE
(DUBLIN END)

GENERAL INFORMATION

Supporters Club Liaison: Gary W. Miller, c/o Club
Telephone Nº: (01475) 888812
Car Parking: At the ground
Coach Parking: James Watt Dock
Nearest Railway Station: Cartsdyke (½ mile)
Nearest Bus Station: Town Centre (1½ miles)
Club Shop: The Morton Club Shop, 85 Cathcart Street, Greenock PA15 1DE
Opening Times: Weekdays 9.00am to 5.00pm. Saturdays 10.00am to 3.00pm
Telephone Nº: (01475) 785855/888812
Postal Sales: Yes
Nearest Police Station: Rue End Street, Greenock
Police Telephone Nº: (01475) 724444

GROUND INFORMATION

Away Supporters' Entrances & Sections:
East Hamilton Street turnstiles

ADMISSION INFO (1999/2000 PRICES)

Adult Standing: £10.00
Adult Seating: £13.00
Child Standing: £6.00
Child Seating: £9.00
Please note that Family Discounts are available
Programme Price: £1.50

DISABLED INFORMATION

Wheelchairs: 5 spaces each for home and away fans accommodated below the Grandstand
Helpers: Please phone the club for information
Prices: Please phone the club for information
Disabled Toilets: None
Are Bookings Necessary: Yes
Contact: (01475) 723571

Travelling Supporters' Information:
Routes: From All Parts: Take the M8 to the A8. Pass through Port Glasgow and turn left after passing the dock-yard buildings on the right-hand side of the road.

HAMILTON ACADEMICAL FC

Founded: 1874 (**Entered League:** 1897)
Former Names: None
Nickname: 'The Accies'
Ground: Firhill Stadium, 80 Firhill Road, Glasgow G20 7AL
Record Attendance: 49,838 (18/2/22)
Note: The club is currently groundsharing with Partick Thistle FC

Colours: Shirts – Red and White Hoops
Shorts – White with Red Flash
Telephone Nº: (01698) 286103
Fax Number: (01698) 285422
Correspondence Address: Enable Building, Prospect House, New Park Street, Hamilton ML3 0BN
Pitch Size: 110 × 75 yards
Ground Capacity: 14,538 (9,076 seats)

NORTH TERRACING

MAIN STAND / FIRHILL ROAD

JACKIE HUSBAND STAND

SOUTH TERRACING

GENERAL INFORMATION

Supporters Club: J. Galloway, c/o Club
Telephone Nº: –
Car Parking: Street parking
Coach Parking: By Police Direction
Nearest Railway Station: Glasgow Queen Street/ Glasgow Central/Maryhill
Nearest Underground Station: St. George's Cross/ Kelvinbridge
Club Shop: Contact the Club Office
Opening Times: Office Hours
Telephone Nº: (01698) 286103
Postal Sales: Yes
Nearest Police Station: Maryhill
Police Telephone Nº: (0141) 532-3700

GROUND INFORMATION

Away Supporters' Entrances & Sections:
All spectators will enter via the Jackie Husband Stand turnstiles

ADMISSION INFO (1999/2000 PRICES)

Adult Seating: £10.00
Child/Senior Citizen Seating: £5.00
Programme Price: £1.00

DISABLED INFORMATION

Wheelchairs: 17 spaces in the North Enclosure
Helpers: Admitted following advance notification
Prices: Free for the disabled and each helper
Disabled Toilets: One available in the Main Stand
Are Bookings Necessary: Yes
Contact: (01698) 286103

Travelling Supporters' Information:
Routes: From the East: Leave the M8 at Junction 16; From the West: Leave the M8 at Junction 17. From both, follow Maryhill Road to Queen's Cross and the ground is on the right.

HEART OF MIDLOTHIAN FC

Founded: 1874 (**Entered League:** 1890)
Former Names: None
Nickname: 'The Jam Tarts' & 'Jambo's'
Ground: Tynecastle Stadium, Gorgie
Road, Edinburgh   EH11 2NL
Record Attendance: 53,496 (13/1/32)
Pitch Size: 107 × 73 yards

Colours: Shirts – Maroon
Shorts – White
Telephone N°: (0131) 200-7200
Ticket Office: (0131) 200-7201
Fax Number: (0131) 200-7222
Ground Capacity: 18,000 (All seats)

GORGIE STAND

McLEOD STREET
MAIN STAND

WHEATFIELD STAND

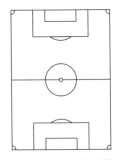

ROSEBURN STAND

GENERAL INFORMATION
Supporters Club: J.N. Borthwick, 21/9 Festival
Gardens, Edinburgh   EH11 1RB
Telephone N°: (0131) 313-4924
Car Parking: Street Parking in Robertson Avenue
and Westfield Road
Coach Parking: Russell Road
Nearest Railway Station: Edinburgh Haymarket
(½ mile)
Nearest Bus Station: St. Andrew's Square
Club Superstore: Gorgie Stand/Tynecastle Terrace
Opening Times: Weekdays 9.30am to 5.30pm and
Matchdays 10.00am to 5.00pm
Telephone N°: (0131) 200-7211
Postal Sales: Yes
Nearest Police Station: Haymarket, Edinburgh
Police Telephone N°: (0131) 229-2323

GROUND INFORMATION
Away Supporters' Entrances & Sections:
Roseburn Stand entrances and accommodation

ADMISSION INFO (1999/2000 PRICES)
Adult Seating: £16.00 – £18.00
Child Seating: £8 or £9 (In the Family Area only)
Programme Price: £1.50

DISABLED INFORMATION
Wheelchairs: 100 spaces available for home and
away fans in Wheatfield, Roseburn & Gorgie Stands
Helpers: Admitted
Prices: Please contact the club for details
Disabled Toilets: Available
Are Bookings Necessary: Yes
Contact: (0131) 200-7222

Travelling Supporters' Information:
Routes: From West: Take A71 (Ayr Road) into Gorgie Road, ground is about ¾ mile past Saughton Park on left;
From North: Take A90 Queensferry Road and turn right into Drum Brae in about ½ mile. Follow Drum Brae
into Meadowplace Road (about 1 mile) then Broomhouse Road to junction with Calder Road. Turn right then as
from West; From South: Take A702/A703 to A720 (Oxgangs Road). Turn left and follow A720 into Wester Hailes
Road (2½ miles) until the junction with Calder Road. Turn right – then as from West.

HIBERNIAN FC

Founded: 1875 (**Entered League:** 1893)
Former Names: None
Nickname: 'The Hi-Bees'
Ground: Easter Road Stadium, Albion Road, Edinburgh   EH7 5QG
Record Attendance: 65,840 (2/1/50)
Pitch Size: 112 × 74 yards

Colours: Shirts – Green and White
Shorts – White
Telephone Nº: (0131) 661-2159
Ticket Office: (0131) 661-1875
Fax Number: (0131) 659-6488
Ground Capacity: 16,032 (All seats)

ALBION PLACE
NEW NORTH STAND
WEST STAND (South) (Centre) (North)
EAST SEATED TERRACE
SOUTH STAND LOWER (Away)
SOUTH STAND UPPER (Home)
ALBION ROAD

GENERAL INFORMATION

Supporters Club: W. Alcorn, 11 Sunnyside, Easter Road Lane, Edinburgh
Telephone Nº: (0131) 661-3157
Car Parking: Street Parking
Coach Parking: By Police Direction
Nearest Railway Station: Edinburgh Waverley (25 minutes walk)
Nearest Bus Station: St. Andrew's Square
Club Shop: North Stand
Opening Times: Tuesday-Friday 9.00am to 5.00pm, Matchdays 9.00am to kick-off
Telephone Nº: (0131) 656-7078
Postal Sales: Yes
Nearest Police Station: Queen Charlotte St., Leith
Police Telephone Nº: (0131) 554-9350

GROUND INFORMATION

Away Supporters' Entrances & Sections:
South Stand (Lower) entrances and accommodation

ADMISSION INFO (1999/2000 PRICES)

Adult Seating: £13.00 – £18.00
Child Seating: £8.00
Programme Price: £1.50

DISABLED INFORMATION

Wheelchairs: 30 spaces in total in the South Seated Enclosure and the North and South Stands
Helpers: One helper admitted per wheelchair
Prices: Free for the disabled. Helpers £18.00
Disabled Toilets: 2 available in the North and South Stands
Are Bookings Necessary: Yes
Contact: (0131) 661-2159

Travelling Supporters' Information:
Routes: From West & North: Take A90 Queensferry Road to A902 and continue for 2¼ miles. Turn right into Great Junction Street and follow into Duke Street then Lochend Road. Turn sharp right into Hawkhill Avenue at Lochend Park and follow road into Albion Place for Ground; From South: Take A1 through Musselburgh (Milton Road/Willow Brae/London Road) and turn right into Easter Road after about 2½ miles. Take 4th right into Albion Road for Ground.

INVERNESS CALEDONIAN THISTLE FC

Founded: 1994 **(Entered League:** 1994)
Former Names: Caledonian Thistle FC
Nickname: 'The Jags' or 'The Blues'
Ground: Caledonian Stadium, East
Longman, Inverness   IV1 1FF
Record Attendance: 9,370 (Telford Street)
(1/3/58)
Colours: Shirts – Royal blue/white + red stripes
Shorts – White

Telephone Nº: (01463) 222880 (Ground)
Ticket Office: Contact Secretary
Fax Number: (01463) 715816
Pitch Size: 115 × 80 yards
Ground Capacity: 6,000
Seating Capacity: 2,000 (approximately)
Contact Address: Mr. J. Falconer,
17 Culloden Park, Inverness
Contact Phone Nº: (01463) 792358

GENERAL INFORMATION

Supporters Club: c/o Club
Telephone Nº: (01463) 222880
Car Parking: At the ground
Coach Parking: At the ground
Nearest Railway Station: Inverness (1 mile)
Nearest Bus Station: Inverness
Club Shop: Yes
Opening Times: Matchdays Only
Telephone Nº: (01463) 222880
Postal Sales: Yes
Nearest Police Station: Longman Road, Inverness
Police Telephone Nº: (01463) 704006

GROUND INFORMATION

Away Supporters' Entrances & Sections:
Accommodation on the East Side of the Main Stand

ADMISSION INFO (1999/2000 PRICES)

Adult Standing: £9.00
Adult Seating: £11.00
Child Standing: £5.00
Child Seating: £6.00
Programme Price: £1.00

DISABLED INFORMATION

Wheelchairs: 16 spaces available in total
Helpers: Please phone the club for details
Prices: Please phone the club for details
Disabled Toilets: Yes
Are Bookings Necessary: Yes
Contact: (01463) 222880

Travelling Supporters' Information:
Routes: The ground is adjacent to Kessock Bridge. From the South: Take the A9 to Inverness and turn right at the roundabout before the bridge over the Moray Firth; From the North: Take the A9 over the bridge and turn left at the roundabout for the ground.

KILMARNOCK FC

Founded: 1869 (**Entered League:** 1896)	**Colours:** Shirts – Blue & White Stripes
Former Names: None	Shorts – White
Nickname: 'Killie'	**Telephone Nº:** (01563) 525184
Ground: Rugby Park, Rugby Road,	**Fax Number:** (01563) 522181
Kilmarnock, Ayrshire KA1 2DP	**Ground Capacity:** 18,218 (all seats)
Record Attendance: 34,246 (17/8/63)	
Pitch Size: 115 × 74 yards	

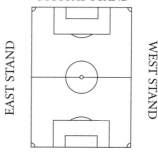

DUNDONALD ROAD END
MOFFAT STAND

EAST STAND

WEST STAND

CHADWICK STAND (Away)
(RUGBY ROAD END)

GENERAL INFORMATION

Supporters Club: c/o Club
Telephone Nº: (01563) 528280
Car Parking: At the ground (Permit Holders only)
Coach Parking: Fairyhill Road Bus Park
Nearest Railway Station: Kilmarnock (15 mins. walk)
Nearest Bus Station: Kilmarnock (10 mins. walk)
Club Shop: Sports Division, Glencairn Square, Kilmarnock
Opening Times: Monday to Saturday 9.00am to 5.00pm
Telephone Nº: (01563) 534210
Postal Sales: Yes
Nearest Police Station: St. Marnock Street, Kilmarnock
Police Telephone Nº: (01563) 521188

GROUND INFORMATION

Away Supporters' Entrances & Sections:
Rugby Road turnstiles for the Chadwick Stand

ADMISSION INFO (1999/2000 PRICES)

Adult Seating: £13.00 – £14.00
Child Seating: £7.00
Programme Price: £1.50

DISABLED INFORMATION

Wheelchairs: 15 spaces each for home and away fans in the Main Stand
Helpers: One helper admitted per wheelchair
Prices: Please phone the club for details
Disabled Toilets: 2 available in the Chadwick Stand and Moffat Stand
Are Bookings Necessary: Yes
Contact: (01292) 288905

Travelling Supporters' Information:
Routes: From Glasgow/Ayr: Take the A77 Kilmarnock Bypass. Exit at the Bellfield Interchange. Take the A71 (Irvine) to the first roundabout then take the A759 (Kilmarnock Town Centre). The ground is ½ mile on the left hand side.

LIVINGSTON FC

Founded: 1943 **(Entered League:** 1974)	**Colours:** Shirts – Amber with Black trim
Former Names: Ferranti Thistle FC,	Shorts – Amber with Black trim
Meadowbank Thistle FC	**Telephone Nº:** (01506) 417000
Nickname: 'The Lions'	**Ticket Office:** (01506) 417000
Ground: Almondvale Stadium,	**Fax Number:** (01506) 418888
Alderstone Road, Livingston EH54 7DN	**Pitch Size:** 105 × 72 yards
Record Attendance: 5,900 (13/2/99)	**Ground Capacity:** 6,107 (All seats)

NORTH STAND

WEST STAND

EAST STAND (Away)

GENERAL INFORMATION

Supporters Club: Duncan Bennett, 63 Granby Avenue, Howden, Livingston EH54 6LD
Telephone Nº: (01506) 495113
Car Parking: Car Park at the ground
Coach Parking: At the ground
Nearest Railway Station: Livingston
Nearest Bus Station: Livingston
Club Shop: Beneath the West Stand
Opening Times: Matchdays and by request in the week
Telephone Nº: (01506) 417000
Postal Sales: Yes
Nearest Police Station: Livingston
Police Telephone Nº: (01506) 431200

GROUND INFORMATION

Away Supporters' Entrances & Sections:
East or North Stand entrances and accommodation

ADMISSION INFO (1999/2000 PRICES)

Adult Seating: £8.00
Child Seating: £4.00
Programme Price: £1.50

DISABLED INFORMATION

Wheelchairs: Accommodated
Helpers: Please phone the club for information
Prices: Please phone the club for information
Disabled Toilets: Yes
Are Bookings Necessary: Yes
Contact: (01506) 417000

Travelling Supporters' Information:
Routes: Exit the M8 at the Livingston turn-off and take the A899 to the Cousland Interchange. Turn right into Cousland Road, pass the Hospital, then turn left into Alderstone Road and the stadium is on the left opposite the Campus.

MONTROSE FC

Founded: 1879 (**Entered League:** 1929)
Former Names: None
Nickname: 'Gable Endies'
Ground: Links Park Stadium, Wellington Street, Montrose   DD10 8QD
Record Attendance: 8,983 (17/3/73)
Pitch Size: 113 × 70 yards

Colours: Shirts – Royal Blue & White stripes
Shorts – Royal Blue
Telephone Nº: (01674) 673200
Ticket Office: (01674) 673200
Fax Number: (01674) 677311
Ground Capacity: 4,500
Seating Capacity: 1,338

WELLINGTON STREET

MAIN STAND

WELLINGTON PARK

UNION ROW

GENERAL INFORMATION

Supporters Club: c/o Links Park
Telephone Nº: –
Car Parking: At the ground and Street Parking also
Coach Parking: Mid Links
Nearest Railway Station: Montrose Western Road
Nearest Bus Station: High Street, Montrose
Club Shop: At ground
Opening Times: Fridays and Matchdays 10.00am to 5.00pm
Telephone Nº: (01674) 673200
Postal Sales: Yes
Nearest Police Station: George Street, Montrose (15 minutes walk)
Police Telephone Nº: (01674) 672222

GROUND INFORMATION

Away Supporters' Entrances & Sections:
No usual segregation

ADMISSION INFO (1999/2000 PRICES)

Adult Standing: £7.00
Adult Seating: £7.50
Child Standing: £3.50
Child Seating: £4.00
Programme Price: £1.00

DISABLED INFORMATION

Wheelchairs: 5 spaces available in the Main Stand
Helpers: Please phone the club for information
Prices: Please phone the club for information
Disabled Toilets: 2 available in the Main Stand
Are Bookings Necessary: No, but they are helpful
Contact: (01674) 673200

Travelling Supporters' Information:
Routes: Take the main A92 Coastal Road to Montrose. Once in the town, the ground is well signposted and is situated in the Mid-Links area.

MOTHERWELL FC

Founded: 1886 **(Entered League:** 1893)
Former Names: None
Nickname: 'The Well'
Ground: Fir Park, Fir Park Street, Motherwell ML1 2QN
Record Attendance: 35,632 (12/3/52)
Pitch Size: 110 × 75 yards

Colours: Shirts – Amber with claret hoop
Shorts – White
Telephone Nº: (01698) 333333
Ticket Office: (01698) 333030
Fax Number: (01698) 338001
Ground Capacity: 13,742

D. COOPER STAND

(FIR PARK STREET)
MAIN STAND

EAST STAND

(Away)
SOUTH STAND

GENERAL INFORMATION

Supporters Club: Jim Frame, c/o Fir Park
Telephone Nº: –
Car Parking: Street Parking and nearby Car Parks
Coach Parking: Orbiston Street
Nearest Railway Station: Motherwell (1½ miles)
Nearest Bus Station: Motherwell
Club Shop: At ground
Opening Times: Saturday Matchdays 10.00am to 5.00pm
Telephone Nº: (01698) 333333
Postal Sales: Yes
Nearest Police Station: Motherwell (¼ mile)
Police Telephone Nº: (01698) 483000

GROUND INFORMATION

Away Supporters' Entrances & Sections:
Dalziel Drive entrances for the South Stand

ADMISSION INFO (1999/2000 PRICES)

Adult Seating: £12.00 – £17.00
Child Seating: £6.00 – £8.00
Note: Discounts are available in the Family Section
Programme Price: £1.50

DISABLED INFORMATION

Wheelchairs: 12 spaces for home fans and 6 spaces for away fans in the South-West enclosure.
Helpers: Admitted
Prices: Please phone the club for information
Disabled Toilets: One available close to the Disabled Area
Are Bookings Necessary: Yes – 1 week in advance
Contact: (01698) 333333

Travelling Supporters' Information:
Routes: From East: Take A723 into Merry Street and turn right into Brandon Street (1 mile). Follow through to Windmill Hill Street and turn right at Fire Station into Knowetop Avenue for Ground; From Elsewhere: Exit M74 Junction 4 and take A723 Hamilton Road into Town Centre. Turn right into Brandon Street then as from East.

PARTICK THISTLE FC

Founded: 1876 **(Entered League:** 1890)
Former Names: None
Nickname: 'The Jags'
Ground: Firhill Stadium, 80 Firhill Road,
Glasgow G20 7AL
Record Attendance: 49,838 (18/2/22)
Pitch Size: 110 × 75 yards

Colours: Shirts – Red and Yellow Hoops
Shorts – White
Telephone Nº: (0141) 579-1971
Ticket Office: (0141) 579-1971
Fax Number: (0141) 945-1525
Ground Capacity: 14,538
Seating Capacity: 8,397

NORTH TERRACING

MAIN STAND
FIRHILL ROAD

JACKIE HUSBAND STAND

SOUTH TERRACING

GENERAL INFORMATION

Supporters Club: c/o Partick Thistle F.C., Firhill
Stadium, Glasgow G20 7AL
Car Parking: Street Parking
Coach Parking: By Police Direction
Nearest Railway Station: Maryhill
Nearest Underground Station: St. George's Cross
Club Shops: At the Stadium
Opening Times: Matchdays 11.30am to 5.00pm or
5.00pm to 9.30pm for Night matches. Also
Wednesdays 12.00pm to 4.00pm
Telephone Nº: (0141) 579-1971
Postal Sales: Yes
Nearest Police Station: Maryhill
Police Telephone Nº: (0141) 532-3700

GROUND INFORMATION

Away Supporters' Entrances & Sections:
At the North end of the Jackie Husband Stand

ADMISSION INFO (1999/2000 PRICES)

Adult Seating: £10.00
Senior Citizen/Child Seating: £5.00
Programme Price: £1.50

DISABLED INFORMATION

Wheelchairs: 17 spaces in the North Enclosure
Helpers: One helper admitted per wheelchair
Prices: Free for the disabled. Helpers pay £10.00
Disabled Toilets: One available in the Main Stand
Are Bookings Necessary: Yes – contact the Club
Secretary
Contact: (0141) 579-1971

Travelling Supporters' Information:
Routes: From the East: Leave the M8 at Junction 16; From the West: Leave the M8 at Junction 17. From both,
follow Maryhill Road to Queen's Cross and the ground is on the right.

QUEEN OF THE SOUTH FC

Founded: 1919 (**Entered League**: 1923)	**Colours**: Shirts – Blue
Former Names: None	Shorts – Blue
Nickname: 'The Doonhamers'	**Telephone Nº**: (01387) 254853
Ground: Palmerston Park, Terregles	**Ticket Office**: (01387) 254853
Street, Dumfries DG2 9BA	**Fax Number**: (01387) 254853
Record Attendance: 24,500 (23/2/52)	**Ground Capacity**: 6,412
Pitch Size: 112 × 73 yards	**Seating Capacity**: 3,509

PORTLAND ROAD

WEST STAND

EAST STAND (Away)

(Away)
TERREGLES STREET END

GENERAL INFORMATION

Supporters Club: G. Corbett, 12 Loch Road, Dumfries
Telephone Nº: (01387) 262180
Car Parking: Car Park adjacent to the ground
Coach Parking: Car Park adjacent to the ground
Nearest Railway Station: Dumfries (¾ mile)
Nearest Bus Station: Dumfries Whitesands (5 minutes walk)
Club Shop: At ground
Opening Times: Daily
Telephone Nº: (01387) 254853
Postal Sales: Yes – Contact the Club
Nearest Police Station: Dumfries (½ mile)
Police Telephone Nº: (01387) 252112

GROUND INFORMATION

Away Supporters' Entrances & Sections:
Terregles Street entrances for the Terregles End and part of the East Stand

ADMISSION INFO (1999/2000 PRICES)

Adult Standing: £8.00
Adult Seating: £8.00
Child Standing: £3.00
Child Seating: £6.00
Programme Price: £1.10

DISABLED INFORMATION

Wheelchairs: Accommodated in front of the East Stand
Helpers: Please phone the club for details
Prices: Please phone the club for details
Disabled Toilets: One available in the East Stand
Are Bookings Necessary: Yes
Contact: (01387) 254853

Travelling Supporters' Information:
Routes: From East: Take the A75 to Dumfries and follow ring road over the River Nith. Turn left at 1st roundabout then right at 2nd roundabout (the Kilmarnock/Glasgow Road roundabout). Ground is a short way along adjacent to the Tesco store; From West: Take the A75 to Dumfries and proceed along ring road to 1st roundabout (Kilmarnock/Glasgow Road) then as East; From North: Take the A76 to Dumfries and carry straight across 1st roundabout for ground.

QUEEN'S PARK FC

Founded: 1867 (**Entered League:** 1900)
Former Names: None
Nickname: 'The Spiders'
Ground: Hampden Park, Mount Florida, Glasgow   G42 9BA
Record Attendance: 150,239 (17/4/37)
Pitch Size: 115 × 75 yards

Colours: Shirts – Black and White Hoops
Shorts – White
Telephone Nº: (0141) 632-1275
Ticket Office: (0141) 632-1275
Fax Number: (0141) 636-1612
Ground Capacity: 52,000 (All seats)

WEST STAND

SOUTH STAND

NORTH STAND

EAST STAND

GENERAL INFORMATION

Supporters Club: K. McAllister, 58 Brunton Street, Glasgow   G44
Telephone Nº: (0141) 637-6075
Car Parking: Car Park at the Stadium
Coach Parking: Car Park at the Stadium
Nearest Railway Station: Mount Florida and King's Park (both 5 minutes walk)
Nearest Bus Station: Buchanan Street
Club Shop: At the ground
Opening Times: During home matches only
Telephone Nº: (0141) 632-1275
Postal Sales: Yes
Nearest Police Station: Aikenhead Road, Glasgow
Police Telephone Nº: (0141) 532-4900

GROUND INFORMATION

Away Supporters' Entrances & Sections: South Stand

ADMISSION INFO (1999/2000 PRICES)
Adult Seating: £7.00
Child Seating: £3.00
Programme Price: £1.00

DISABLED INFORMATION
Wheelchairs: 160 spaces available in total
Helpers: Admitted
Prices: Free for the disabled. Helpers normal prices
Disabled Toilets: Available
Are Bookings Necessary: Yes
Contact: (0141) 632-1275

Travelling Supporters' Information:
Routes: From the South: Take the A724 to the Cambuslang Road and at Eastfield branch left into Main Street and follow through Burnhill Street and Westmuir Place into Prospecthill Road. Turn left into Aikenhead Road and right into Mount Annan for Kinghorn Drive and the Stadium; From the South: Take the A77 Fenwick Road, through Kilmarnock Road into Pollokshaws Road then turn right into Langside Avenue. Pass through Battle Place to Battlefield Road and turn left into Cathcart Road. Turn right into Letherby Drive, right into Carmunnock Road and 1st left into Mount Annan Drive for the Stadium; From the North & East: Exit M8 Junction 15 and passing Infirmary on left proceed into High Street and cross the Albert Bridge into Crown Street. Join Cathcart Road and proceed South until it becomes Carmunnock Road. Turn left into Mount Annan Drive and left again into Kinghorn Drive for the Stadium.

RAITH ROVERS FC

Founded: 1883 (**Entered League:** 1902)
Former Names: None
Nickname: 'The Rovers'
Ground: Stark's Park, Pratt Street, Kirkcaldy KY1 1SA
Record Attendance: 31,306 (7/2/53)
Pitch Size: 113 × 67 yards

Colours: Shirts – Navy with White Trim
Shorts – White with Navy Trim
Telephone Nº: (01592) 263514
Ticket Office: (01592) 263514
Fax Number: (01592) 642833
Ground Capacity: 10,271 (all seats)

SOUTH STAND

MAIN STAND

RAILWAY STAND (Away)

(Away)
NORTH STAND
KINCARDINE BRIDGE ROAD

GENERAL INFORMATION

Supporters Club: F. Hamilton, 22 Tower Terrace, Kirkcaldy
Telephone Nº: (01592) 653927
Car Parking: Esplanade and Beveridge Car Park
Coach Parking: Railway Station & Esplanade
Nearest Railway Station: Kirkcaldy (15 mins. walk)
Nearest Bus Station: Kirkcaldy (15 minutes walk)
Club Shop: At the ground (matchdays only) and also at Sports Division, Retail Park, Kirkcaldy
Opening Times: Sports Division is open 7 days a week
Telephone Nº: (01592) 263514
Postal Sales: Yes
Nearest Police Station: St. Brycedale Road, Kirkcaldy (15 minutes walk)
Police Telephone Nº: (01592) 418700

GROUND INFORMATION

Away Supporters' Entrances & Sections:
Entrances for the North Stand and part of the Railway Stand

ADMISSION INFO (1999/2000 PRICES)

Adult Seating: £11.00
Child Seating: £6.00
Programme Price: £1.50

DISABLED INFORMATION

Wheelchairs: 12 spaces each for home and away fans accommodated in the North & South Stands
Helpers: One helper admitted per wheelchair
Prices: Free of charge for the disabled. Helpers pay the concessionary price
Disabled Toilets: Available in North & South Stands
Are Bookings Necessary: Only for all-ticket games
Contact: (01592) 263514

Travelling Supporters' Information:
Routes: Take the M8 to the end then follow the A90/M90 over the Forth Road Bridge. Exit the M90 at Junction 1 and follow the A921 to Kirkcaldy. On the outskirts of tow, turn left at the B & Q roundabout from which the floodlights can be seen. The ground is raised on the hill nearby.

RANGERS FC

Founded: 1873 (**Entered League:** 1890)
Former Names: None
Nickname: 'The Gers' or 'Light Blues'
Ground: Ibrox Stadium, 150 Edmiston Drive, Glasgow   G51 2XD
Record Attendance: 118,567 (2/1/39)
Pitch Size: 125 × 89 yards

Colours: Shirts – Blue with White Trim
Shorts – White
Telephone N°: (0870) 600-1972
Ticket Office: (0870) 600-1993
Fax Number: (0870) 600-1978
Ground Capacity: 50,403 (All seats)

BROOMLOAN ROAD STAND
(Away)

EDMISTON DRIVE (EAST) MAIN STAND (WEST)

(WEST) GOVAN STAND (EAST)

COPLAND ROAD STAND

GENERAL INFORMATION

Supporters Club: The Secretary, Rangers Supporters' Association, 250 Edmiston Drive, Glasgow
Telephone N°: (0141) 427-2902
Car Parking: Albion Car Park
Coach Parking: By Police direction
Nearest Railway Station: Ibrox (Underground) – 2 minutes walk
Nearest Bus Station: Glasgow City Centre
Club Shop: The Rangers Superstore, Ibrox Stadium
Opening Times: Monday to Saturday 9.00am to 5.30pm; Sundays 11.00am to 5.00pm and also open one hour after the end of the game
Telephone N°: (0870) 600-1972
Postal Sales: Yes – Rangers Direct (0990) 991997
Nearest Police Station: Strathclyde Police G Div., 923 Helen Street
Police Telephone N°: (0141) 445-1113

GROUND INFORMATION

Away Supporters' Entrances & Sections: Broomloan Road Turnstiles for Broomloan Road Stand

ADMISSION INFO (1999/2000 PRICES)

Adult Seating: £17.00 – £22.00
Child Seating: £10.00 – £11.00
Other Concessions: £13.00 – £15.00
Note: Most of the ground capacity is taken by season-ticket holders
Programme Price: £1.50

DISABLED INFORMATION

Wheelchairs: 60 spaces for home fans, 5 for away fans in front of the West Enclosure
Helpers: Admitted
Prices: Free of charge for the disabled and helpers if they are members of the Disabled Supporters' Club
Disabled Toilets: Available in the West Enclosure
Are Bookings Necessary: Yes
Contact: (0870) 600-1972

Travelling Supporters' Information:
Routes: From All Parts: Exit the M8 at Junction 23. The road leads straight to the Stadium.

ROSS COUNTY FC

Founded: 1929 (**Entered League:** 1994)	**Colours:** Shirts – Navy Blue
Former Names: None	Shorts – White
Nickname: 'The County'	**Telephone Nº:** (01349) 860860
Ground: Victoria Park, Dingwall,	**Ticket Office:** (01349) 860860
Ross-shire IV15 9QW	**Fax Number:** (01349) 866277
Record Attendance: 10,000 (19/2/66)	**Ground Capacity:** 6,500
Pitch Size: 110 × 72 yards	**Seating Capacity:** 1,519

WEST STAND

EAST STAND

GENERAL INFORMATION

Supporters Club: B. Campbell, c/o Victoria Park
Telephone Nº: (01349) 862253
Car Parking: At the ground
Coach Parking: At the ground
Nearest Railway Station: Dingwall (adjacent)
Nearest Bus Station: Dingwall
Club Shop: At ground
Opening Times: Weekdays and Matchdays
Telephone Nº: (01349) 862253
Postal Sales: Yes
Nearest Police Station: Dingwall
Police Telephone Nº: (01349) 862444

GROUND INFORMATION

Away Supporters' Entrances & Sections:
East Stand entrances and accommodation

ADMISSION INFO (1999/2000 PRICES)

Adult Standing: £8.00
Adult Seating: £9.00
Child Standing: £4.00
Child Seating: £5.00 (Children accompanied by an adult cost £2.00 each)
Programme Price: £1.00

DISABLED INFORMATION

Wheelchairs: 6 spaces each for home and away fans
Helpers: Admitted
Prices: Normal prices are charged
Disabled Toilets: Available at the bottom of the West Stand
Are Bookings Necessary: Yes
Contact: (01349) 862253

Travelling Supporters' Information:
Routes: The ground is situated at Dingwall adjacent to the Railway Station which is down Jubilee Park Road at the bottom of the High Street.

St. Johnstone FC

<table>
<tr><td>

Founded: 1884 (**Entered League:** 1911)
Former Names: None
Nickname: 'Saints'
Ground: McDiarmid Park, Crieff Road,
Perth PH1 2SJ
Record Attendance: 10,545 (23/5/99)
Pitch Size: 115 × 75 yards

</td><td>

Colours: Shirts – Blue
         Shorts – White
Telephone Nº: (01738) 459090
Ticket Office: (01738) 459090
Fax Number: (01738) 625771
Ground Capacity: 10,673 (All seats)

</td></tr>
</table>

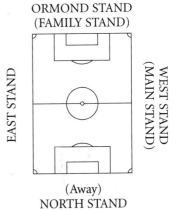

ORMOND STAND
(FAMILY STAND)

EAST STAND

WEST STAND
(MAIN STAND)

(Away)
NORTH STAND

GENERAL INFORMATION

Supporters Club: J. McLeish, 157 Dunkeld Road,
Perth PH1 3AE
Telephone Nº: (01738) 442022
Car Parking: Car park at the ground
Coach Parking: At the ground
Nearest Railway Station: Perth (3 miles)
Nearest Bus Station: Perth (3 miles)
Club Shop: At ground
Opening Times: 9.00am to 5.00pm
Telephone Nº: (01738) 459090
Postal Sales: Yes
Nearest Police Station: Perth (1½ miles)
Police Telephone Nº: (01738) 621141

GROUND INFORMATION

Away Supporters' Entrances & Sections:
North Stand Side entrances for accommodation in
the North Stand and North End of the West Stand

ADMISSION INFO (1999/2000 PRICES)

Adult Seating: £11.00 – £15.00
Child Seating: £5.00 – £9.00
Note: Reduced rates available in the Family Stand
Programme Price: £1.50

DISABLED INFORMATION

Wheelchairs: 10 spaces each available for home and
away fans in the East and West Stands
Helpers: Please phone the club for details
Prices: Please phone the club for details
Disabled Toilets: 2 available in both the East and
West Stands
Are Bookings Necessary: Yes
Contact: (01738) 459090

Travelling Supporters' Information:
Routes: Follow the M80 to Stirling, take the A9 Inverness Road north from Perth and follow the signs for the
'Football Stadium'. The ground is situated beside a dual-carriageway – the Perth Western By-pass near Junction
11 of the M90.

St. Mirren FC

Founded: 1877 (**Entered League:** 1890)
Former Names: None
Nickname: 'The Saints' or 'The Buddies'
Ground: St. Mirren Park, Love Street,
Paisley PA3 2EJ
Record Attendance: 47,428 (7/3/25)
Pitch Size: 110 × 70 yards

Colours: Shirts – Black and White Stripes
    Shorts – White
Telephone Nº: (0141) 889-2558
Ticket Office: (0141) 889-2558
Fax Number: (0141) 848-6444
Ground Capacity: 15,410
Seating Capacity: 9,395

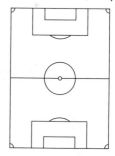

WEST STAND (Away)

(ALBION STREET)
MAIN STAND

WEST
NORTH STAND
EAST

EAST TERRACING
(LOVE STREET)

GENERAL INFORMATION

Supporters Club: Ian Cuthbertson, Knox Street, Paisley
Telephone Nº: (0141) 887-2101
Car Parking: Street Parking
Coach Parking: Clark Street (off Greenock Road – 300 yards)
Nearest Railway Station: Paisley Gilmour Street (400 yards)
Nearest Bus Station: Paisley
Club Shop: In the West Stand
Opening Times: Daily from 8.00am to 10.00pm
Telephone Nº: (0141) 840-1337
Postal Sales: Yes
Nearest Police Station: Mill Street, Paisley (1 mile)
Police Telephone Nº: (0141) 889-1113

GROUND INFORMATION

Away Supporters' Entrances & Sections:
Entrances on West of Main Stand for West Stand

ADMISSION INFO (1999/2000 PRICES)

Adult Standing: £9.00
Adult Seating: £10.00 – £11.00
Child Standing: £4.50
Child Seating: £5.00 – £5.50
Note: Additional child concessions are available for early arrival
Programme Price: £1.50

DISABLED INFORMATION

Wheelchairs: Accommodated in the West Stand
Helpers: Admitted
Prices: Free of charge for both disabled and helpers
Disabled Toilets: 2 available in the West Stand
Are Bookings Necessary: Yes
Contact: (0141) 840-1337

Travelling Supporters' Information:
Routes: From All Parts: Exit the M8 at Junction 29 and take the A726 Greenock Road. The ground is approximately ½ mile along on the left – the floodlights make it clearly visible from some distance.

STENHOUSEMUIR FC

Founded: 1884 **(Entered League:** 1921)
Former Names: Heather Rangers FC
Nickname: 'Warriors'
Ground: Ochilview Park, Gladstone
Road, Stenhousemuir FK5 5QL
Record Attendance: 12,500 (11/3/50)
Pitch Size: 110 × 72 yards

Colours: Shirts – Maroon
        Shorts – White
Telephone Nº: (01324) 562992
Ticket Office: (01324) 562992
Fax Number: (01324) 562980
Ground Capacity: 2,654
Seating Capacity: 628

TRYST ROAD

GLADSTONE ROAD STAND

TERRACING

GENERAL INFORMATION

Supporters Club: A. McNeill, c/o Club
Telephone Nº: (01324) 562992
Car Parking: Large Car Park adjacent
Coach Parking: Behind the North Terracing
Nearest Railway Station: Larbert (1 mile)
Nearest Bus Station: Falkirk (2½ miles)
Club Shop: At ground
Opening Times: Weekdays from 9.00am to 5.00pm
and also 1 hour before and after home games
Telephone Nº: (01324) 562992
Postal Sales: Yes
Nearest Police Station: Stenhousemuir (½ mile)
Police Telephone Nº: (01324) 562112

GROUND INFORMATION

Away Supporters' Entrances & Sections:
Terracing entrances and accommodation

ADMISSION INFO (1999/2000 PRICES)

Adult Standing: £8.00
Adult Seating: £9.00
Senior Citizen/Child Standing: £4.00
Senior Citizen/Child Seating: £4.50
Note: Additional Family Discounts are available
Programme Price: £1.00

DISABLED INFORMATION

Wheelchairs: Accommodated
Helpers: Admitted
Prices: Normal prices are charged
Disabled Toilets: Available in the New Gladstone
Road Stand
Are Bookings Necessary: No
Contact: (01324) 562992

Travelling Supporters' Information:
Routes: Exit the M876 at Junction 2 and follow signs for Stenhousemuir. Pass the Old Hospital and turn right after the Golf Course. The ground is on the left behind the houses – the floodlights are visible for ¼ mile.

STIRLING ALBION FC

Founded: 1945 (**Entered League:** 1946)
Former Names: None
Nickname: 'The Albion'
Ground: Forth Bank Stadium, Spring Kerse, Stirling   FK7 7UJ
Record Attendance: 3,808 (17/2/96)
Pitch Size: 110 × 74 yards

Colours: Shirts – Red with White Sleeves
                   Shorts – White
Telephone Nº: (01786) 450399
Ticket Office: (01786) 450399
Fax Number: (01786) 448592
Ground Capacity: 3,808
Seating Capacity: 2,500

NORTH TERRACING

WEST STAND

EAST STAND

(Away)
SOUTH TERRACING

GENERAL INFORMATION
Supporters Club: S. Torrance, c/o Club
Telephone Nº: –
Car Parking: Large Car Park adjacent to the ground
Coach Parking: Adjacent to the ground
Nearest Railway Station: Stirling (2 miles)
Nearest Bus Station: Stirling (2 miles)
Club Shop: Yes
Opening Times: Matchdays Only
Telephone Nº: (01786) 450399
Postal Sales: Yes
Nearest Police Station: Stirling (2 miles)
Police Telephone Nº: (01786) 456000

GROUND INFORMATION
Away Supporters' Entrances & Sections:
South Terracing entrances and accommodation.

ADMISSION INFO (1999/2000 PRICES)
Adult Standing: £8.00
Adult Seating: £9.00
Child Standing: £4.50
Child Seating: £5.00
Note: Standing admission is only available for certain games
Programme Price: £1.00

DISABLED INFORMATION
Wheelchairs: 18 spaces available each for home and away fans
Helpers: Admitted
Prices: Free of charge for the disabled
Disabled Toilets: 2 available beneath each stand
Are Bookings Necessary: No
Contact: (01786) 450399

Travelling Supporters' Information:
Routes: Follow signs for Stirling from the M9/M80 Northbound. From Pirnhall Roundabout follow signs for Alloa/St. Andrew's to the 4th roundabout and then turn left for the stadium.

STRANRAER FC

Founded: 1870 (**Entered League:** 1955)
Former Names: None
Nickname: 'The Blues'
Ground: Stair Park, London Road, Stranraer DG9 8BS
Record Attendance: 6,500 (24/1/48)
Pitch Size: 110 × 70 yards

Colours: Shirts – Blue
Shorts – White
Telephone Nº: (01776) 703271
Ticket Office: (01776) 703271
Fax Number: (01776) 702194
Ground Capacity: 5,500
Seating Capacity: 1,900

GENERAL INFORMATION

Supporters Club: Mrs. Margaret Rennie, 18 Eastwood Avenue, Stranraer
Telephone Nº: (01776) 706563
Car Parking: Car Park at the ground
Coach Parking: Port Rodie, Stranraer
Nearest Railway Station: Stranraer (1 mile)
Nearest Bus Station: Port Rodie, Stranraer
Club Shop: At the ground
Opening Times: 2.30pm to 3.00pm and during half-time on Matchdays only
Telephone Nº: –
Postal Sales: Write to 28 Springfield Crescent, Stranraer
Nearest Police Station: Stranraer (¾ mile)
Police Telephone Nº: (01776) 702112

GROUND INFORMATION

Away Supporters' Entrances & Sections:
London Road entrances for the Visitors Stand

ADMISSION INFO (1999/2000 PRICES)

Adult Standing: £8.00
Adult Seating: £10.00
Child Standing: £4.00
Child Seating: £6.00
Programme Price: £1.00

DISABLED INFORMATION

Wheelchairs: 6 spaces each for Home and Away fans in front of the North Stand and South Stand
Helpers: Please phone the club for details
Prices: Please phone the club for details
Disabled Toilets: One available each in the North and South Stands
Are Bookings Necessary: Yes
Contact: (01776) 702194

Travelling Supporters' Information:
Routes: From the West: Take the A75 to Stranraer and the ground is on the left-hand side of the road in a public park shortly after entering the town; From the North: Take the A77 and follow it to where it joins with the A75 (then as West). The ground is set back from the road and the floodlights are clearly visible.

NOTE: Club Call numbers are charged at premium rates

Aberdeen
Web site: www.afc.co.uk
Club Call Nº: (09068) 121551

Airdrieonians
Web site: www.airdrieoniansfc.com
Club Call Nº: −

Albion Rovers
Web site: −
Club Call Nº: −

Alloa Athletic
Web site: −
Club Call Nº: −

Arbroath
Web site: −
Club Call Nº: −

Ayr United
Web site: −
Club Call Nº: (09068) 121552

Berwick Rangers
Web site: www.brfc.mcmail.com
Club Call Nº: (09068) 800697

Brechin City
Web site: www.brechincity.co.uk
Club Call Nº: −

Celtic
Web site: www.celticfc.co.uk
Club Call Nº: (09068) 196721

Clyde
Web site: www.clydefc.co.uk
Club Call Nº: −

Clydebank
Web site: −
Club Call Nº: −

Cowdenbeath
Web site: −
Club Call Nº: −

Dumbarton
Web site: −
Club Call Nº: −

Dundee
Web site: www.dundeefc.co.uk
Club Call Nº: −

Dundee United
Web site: −
Club Call Nº: (09068) 881909

Dunfermline Athletic
Web site: −
Club Call Nº: (09066) 555060

East Fife
Web site: −
Club Call Nº: −

East Stirlingshire
Web site: −
Club Call Nº: −

Falkirk
Web site: −
Club Call Nº: −

Forfar Athletic
Web site: −
Club Call Nº: −

Greenock Morton
Web site: www.greenockmorton.co.uk
Club Call Nº: (09066) 555806

Hamilton Academical
Web site: −
Club Call Nº: (09068) 666492

Heart of Midlothian
Web site: www.heartsfc.co.uk
Club Call Nº: (09068) 121183

Hibernian
Web site: www.hibs.co.uk
Club Call Nº: (09068) 707070

NOTE: Club Call numbers are charged at premium rates

Inverness Caledonian Thistle
Web site: –
Club Call Nº: –

Kilmarnock
Web site: www.kilmarnockfc.co.uk
Club Call Nº: (09068) 633269

Livingston
Web site: –
Club Call Nº: (09068) 121974

Montrose
Web site: –
Club Call Nº: –

Motherwell
Web site: –
Club Call Nº: (09068) 121553

Partick Thistle
Web site: –
Club Call Nº: (09068) 666474

Queen of the South
Web site: www.qosfc.co.uk
Club Call Nº: (09066) 555983

Queen's Park
Web site: www.queensparkfc.co.uk
Club Call Nº: –

Raith Rovers
Web site: www.raithrovers.com
Club Call Nº: –

Rangers
Web site: www.rangers.co.uk
Club Call Nº: (09068) 121555

Ross County
Web site: –
Club Call Nº: –

St. Johnstone
Web site: www.stjohnstonefc.co.uk
Club Call Nº: (09068) 121559

St. Mirren
Web site: www.stmirren.com
Club Call Nº: (09068) 121885

Stenhousemuir
Web site: –
Club Call Nº: –

Stirling Albion
Web site: www.stirlingalbion.freeserve.co.uk
Club Call Nº: –

Stranraer
Web site: –
Club Call Nº: –

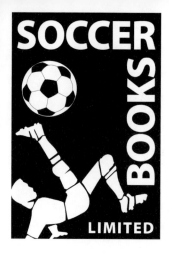

SOCCER BOOKS LIMITED

72 ST. PETERS AVENUE (Dept. SBL)
CLEETHORPES
N.E. LINCOLNSHIRE
DN35 8HU
ENGLAND

Tel. 01472 696226/601893   Fax 01472 698546

Web site http://www.soccer-books.co.uk
e-mail info@soccbook.demon.co.uk

Established in 1982, Soccer Books Limited has now combined its book/video selling business (TH SOCCER BOOKSHELF) with its publishing business (SOCCER BOOK PUBLISHING LIMITED under a single company, to streamline the processing of orders.

Already the suppliers of the biggest range of English-Language soccer books and videos, we are no expanding our stocks even further to include many more titles including German, French, Spanis and Italian-language books.

With over 100,000 satisfied customers already, we supply books to virtually every country in th world but have maintained the friendliness and accessibility associated with a small family-ru business. The range of titles we sell includes:

YEARBOOKS – All major yearbooks including Rothmans (many editions), Calcios (many editions Supporters' Guides, F.A. Yearbooks, Playfair Annuals, North & Latin American Guides (5 editions African Guides, Non-League Directories.

CLUB HISTORIES – Complete Records, Official Histories, 25 Year Records, Definitive Histori plus many more including books on German clubs.

WORLD FOOTBALL – World Cup books, International Line-up & Statistics Series, Europe: Championships History, Guinness Book of World Soccer, International League & Club Histori (many titles) and much more.

BIOGRAPHIES & WHO'S WHOS – Managers: Dalglish, Ferguson, Venables, Paisley, Shank Busby and others; Players: Dicks, Trautmann, Rush, Cantona, Ginola and others; Who's Whc Guinness and others – including clubs.

ENCYCLOPEDIAS & GENERAL TITLES – Football Grounds of Britain, Hooligan studies, Histo of the F.A. Cup, History of the Wembley Cup Final and dozens of others.

VIDEOS – Season's highlights, histories, big games, World Cup, European Championships, play profiles, F.A. Cup Finals – including many back items.

For a current listing of our titles, please contact us using the information at the top of the page.

Scottish Football League Statistics Season 1998/99

Premier League
Home & Away Chart
Final League Table

First Division
Home & Away Chart
Final League Table

Second Division
Home & Away Chart
Final League Table

Third Division
Home & Away Chart
Final League Table

Scottish League Premier Division Season 1998/99	Aberdeen	Celtic	Dundee	Dundee United	Dunfermline Athletic	Heart of Midlothian	Kilmarnock	Motherwell	Rangers	St. Johnstone
Aberdeen	■	3-2	2-2	0-3	2-1	2-0	0-1	1-1	1-1	0-1
	■	1-5	1-2	0-4	3-1	2-5	2-1	1-1	2-4	1-0
Celtic	2-0	■	6-1	2-1	5-0	1-1	1-1	2-0	5-1	0-1
	3-2	■	5-0	2-1	5-0	3-0	1-0	1-0	0-3	5-0
Dundee	0-2	1-1	■	2-2	1-0	1-0	1-1	1-0	0-4	1-1
	1-2	0-3	■	1-3	3-1	2-0	2-1	1-0	1-1	0-1
Dundee United	1-0	1-1	0-1	■	1-1	0-0	0-2	2-2	0-0	1-1
	3-0	1-2	0-2	■	1-1	1-3	0-0	0-3	1-2	0-1
Dunfermline Athletic	1-1	2-2	2-0	2-1	■	1-1	0-3	1-1	0-2	1-1
	1-2	1-2	2-0	2-2	■	0-0	0-6	1-2	0-3	1-0
Heart of Midlothian	2-0	2-1	0-2	0-1	2-1	■	2-1	3-0	2-1	1-1
	0-2	2-4	1-2	4-1	2-0	■	2-2	0-2	2-3	0-2
Kilmarnock	4-0	2-0	2-1	2-0	0-0	3-0	■	0-0	1-3	2-2
	4-2	0-0	0-0	2-0	0-0	1-0	■	0-1	0-5	1-1
Motherwell	2-2	1-2	2-1	1-0	0-0	3-2	0-0	■	1-0	1-0
	1-1	1-7	1-2	2-0	1-1	0-4	1-2	■	1-5	1-2
Rangers	2-1	0-0	1-0	2-1	1-1	3-0	1-0	2-0	■	4-0
	3-1	2-2	6-1	0-1	1-0	0-0	1-1	2-1	■	1-0
St. Johnstone	2-0	2-1	1-1	1-3	1-1	1-1	0-0	5-0	0-7	■
	4-1	1-0	1-0	1-0	1-1	0-0	0-1	0-0	3-1	■

Scottish Premier League

Season 1998/99

Rangers	36	23	8	5	78	31	77
Celtic	36	21	8	7	84	35	71
St. Johnstone	36	15	12	9	39	38	57
Kilmarnock	36	14	14	8	47	29	56
Dundee	36	13	7	16	36	56	46
Heart of Midlothian	36	11	9	16	44	50	42
Motherwell	36	10	11	15	35	54	41
Aberdeen	36	10	7	19	43	71	37
Dundee United	36	8	10	18	37	48	34
Dunfermline Athletic	36	4	16	16	28	59	28

Champions: Rangers

Relegated: Dunfermline Athletic

54

Scottish League Division One Season 1998/99	Airdrieonians	Ayr United	Clydebank	Falkirk	Greenock Morton	Hamilton Academical	Hibernian	Raith Rovers	St. Mirren	Stranraer
Airdrieonians	■	0-2	0-0	0-3	0-1	3-2	1-3	0-1	1-0	3-2
	■	0-2	2-0	1-2	0-2	1-0	1-4	2-2	0-3	2-0
Ayr United	1-2	■	4-1	4-2	1-0	2-3	3-3	0-2	1-1	7-1
	0-1	■	0-0	1-2	1-0	5-0	1-3	1-0	2-2	4-0
Clydebank	0-1	0-1	■	0-1	2-1	0-0	2-2	1-1	1-0	2-1
	0-1	2-1	■	1-2	1-2	0-0	2-0	0-0	2-2	1-2
Falkirk	0-1	1-0	2-2	■	2-1	2-1	1-1	1-1	1-1	1-0
	1-1	3-0	0-2	■	1-2	6-1	1-2	1-0	1-0	3-2
Greenock Morton	0-0	1-2	2-2	0-3	■	1-2	0-1	2-0	0-1	3-0
	0-2	1-4	1-1	3-2	■	3-0	1-3	1-1	0-0	1-0
Hamilton Academical	1-1	1-3	1-2	2-1	0-0	■	2-2	3-2	0-0	1-2
	0-2	0-2	0-1	0-2	0-2	■	0-2	1-2	0-0	1-0
Hibernian	1-0	4-2	2-1	2-1	2-1	0-0	■	3-1	4-1	1-2
	3-0	3-0	3-0	2-1	2-1	4-0	■	5-1	2-1	2-0
Raith Rovers	1-3	0-0	0-1	1-1	0-0	0-2	1-3	■	1-0	2-0
	0-1	2-4	2-1	2-1	1-3	1-1	1-3	■	1-1	3-2
St. Mirren	1-5	0-2	0-0	0-2	1-0	3-2	2-0	2-1	■	1-0
	3-0	1-0	1-1	0-3	1-5	1-0	1-2	3-1	■	5-1
Stranraer	1-2	0-1	0-2	1-2	2-3	2-1	0-1	2-2	0-1	■
	1-2	0-2	0-2	0-1	0-1	2-2	0-4	2-0	1-2	■

Scottish League Division One

Season 1998/99

Hibernian	36	28	5	3	84	33	89
Falkirk	36	20	6	10	60	38	66
Ayr United	36	19	5	12	66	42	62
Airdrieonians	36	18	5	13	42	43	59
St. Mirren	36	14	10	12	42	43	52
Greenock Morton	36	14	7	15	45	41	49
Clydebank	36	11	13	12	36	38	46
Raith Rovers	36	8	11	17	37	57	35
Hamilton Academical	36	6	10	20	30	62	28
Stranraer	36	5	2	29	29	74	17

Promoted: Hibernian

Relegated: Stranraer and Hamilton Academical

55

Scottish League Division Two Season 1998/99	Alloa Athletic	Arbroath	Clyde	East Fife	Forfar Athletic	Inverness Caledonian Thistle	Livingston	Partick Thistle	Queen of the South	Stirling Albion
Alloa Athletic	■	1-1	3-0	5-1	1-2	1-1	3-4	3-1	2-1	7-0
	■	1-2	1-0	3-1	3-1	1-4	1-3	0-1	3-5	2-2
Arbroath	0-2	■	0-0	0-2	2-1	0-1	2-2	1-0	2-1	0-3
	1-2	■	0-3	2-1	2-2	3-1	1-1	2-1	0-2	1-0
Clyde	2-1	3-0	■	0-0	3-1	4-1	1-1	1-2	2-0	2-1
	0-1	1-1	■	1-0	1-0	1-1	0-3	0-1	2-1	4-1
East Fife	2-2	0-3	0-0	■	1-0	1-5	2-3	1-3	2-0	2-3
	0-4	1-2	2-1	■	2-1	3-2	1-1	1-0	0-1	1-0
Forfar Athletic	1-2	1-3	2-2	1-2	■	2-2	1-2	0-1	1-0	1-2
	3-1	5-2	3-1	2-4	■	0-3	1-2	2-1	2-1	3-3
Inverness Caledonian Thistle	3-2	2-1	1-1	4-2	2-2	■	2-1	3-2	3-2	3-1
	1-1	2-0	3-0	4-0	2-0	■	3-1	3-2	1-0	2-2
Livingston	2-1	2-1	2-0	3-1	1-1	2-1	■	1-0	2-0	1-1
	1-0	1-0	2-0	1-0	5-0	4-3	■	1-1	1-2	0-0
Partick Thistle	1-0	2-0	0-2	0-1	2-0	0-1	1-3	■	2-2	1-0
	2-1	0-0	0-1	2-2	1-0	2-1	1-1	■	1-3	0-1
Queen of the South	2-1	0-0	2-1	0-0	3-0	2-2	0-1	0-0	■	2-3
	0-0	3-0	2-1	2-0	0-3	1-1	2-2	2-2	■	3-0
Stirling Albion	4-2	0-1	1-2	3-2	3-1	0-1	1-3	2-0	1-0	■
	1-1	2-1	2-3	0-1	2-2	1-5	0-0	3-0	1-3	■

Scottish League Division Two

Season 1998/99

Livingston	36	22	11	3	66	35	77
Inverness Caledonian Thistle	36	21	9	6	80	48	72
Clyde	36	15	8	13	46	42	53
Queen of the South	36	13	9	14	50	45	48
Alloa Athletic	36	13	7	16	65	56	46
Stirling Albion	36	12	8	16	50	63	44
Arbroath	36	12	8	16	37	52	44
Partick Thistle	36	12	7	17	36	45	43
East Fife	36	12	6	18	42	64	42
Forfar Athletic	36	8	7	21	48	70	31

Promoted: Livingston and Inverness Caledonian Thistle

Relegated: Forfar Athletic and East Fife

Scottish League Division Three Season 1998/99	Albion Rovers	Berwick Rangers	Brechin City	Cowdenbeath	Dumbarton	East Stirlingshire	Montrose	Queen's Park	Ross County	Stenhousemuir
Albion Rovers		1-1	1-4	0-1	0-2	3-1	4-1	2-1	0-8	1-3
		0-3	4-1	1-1	0-2	0-2	0-0	1-0	3-3	1-2
Berwick Rangers	2-1		3-0	3-1	3-1	1-2	1-1	0-3	0-2	1-2
	1-1		2-3	2-1	0-1	1-2	4-1	0-2	2-2	2-1
Brechin City	1-0	1-1		2-1	0-0	0-0	3-0	2-2	0-1	1-0
	3-1	0-3		1-1	3-3	1-0	2-3	1-0	0-1	0-2
Cowdenbeath	2-3	1-1	0-1		0-2	2-1	4-1	0-3	1-2	0-2
	0-2	1-2	0-2		2-1	3-2	1-0	0-0	2-3	0-2
Dumbarton	2-0	0-0	1-2	5-0		2-2	0-2	1-0	1-2	0-2
	1-1	1-1	2-0	6-1		0-2	2-1	0-1	0-0	1-4
East Stirlingshire	0-1	0-0	1-1	1-1	1-2		3-1	1-1	2-2	1-1
	4-1	3-3	4-1	0-0	1-2		2-1	1-1	1-2	1-1
Montrose	1-2	1-1	1-2	1-1	1-1	2-0		1-0	3-6	0-0
	2-3	0-3	1-3	1-2	4-2	1-0		3-0	2-3	1-2
Queen's Park	0-0	1-1	1-1	2-0	0-1	0-4	3-0		4-2	0-0
	0-0	1-1	0-2	2-1	1-1	2-1	1-2		0-3	4-1
Ross County	1-2	3-1	0-1	2-0	2-0	1-0	3-1	5-1		0-1
	2-0	6-0	2-1	1-0	1-2	4-2	3-0	1-2		2-2
Stenhousemuir	4-1	1-2	0-1	1-2	0-3	1-0	4-0	2-1	2-4	
	1-2	1-1	1-0	4-1	0-2	2-2	3-1	4-1	3-2	

Scottish League Division Three

Season 1998/99

Ross County	36	24	5	7	87	42	77
Stenhousemuir	36	19	7	10	62	42	64
Brechin City	36	17	8	11	47	43	59
Dumbarton	36	16	9	11	53	40	57
Berwick Rangers	36	12	14	10	53	49	50
Queen's Park	36	11	11	14	41	46	44
Albion Rovers	36	12	8	16	43	63	44
East Stirlingshire	36	9	13	14	50	48	40
Cowdenbeath	36	8	7	21	34	65	31
Montrose	36	8	6	22	42	74	30

Promoted: Ross County and Stenhousemuir

THE HIGHLAND FOOTBALL LEAGUE

Founded
1893

Secretary
Mr. J.H. Grant

Address
35 Hamilton Drive, Elgin   IV30 2NN

Phone
(01343) 544995

BRORA RANGERS FC

Founded: 1878/79
Former Names: None
Nickname: 'The Cattachs'
Ground: Dudgeon Park, Brora, KW9 6QA
Record Attendance: 2,000 (31/8/63)
Colours: Shirts – Red with White Pin Stripes
Shorts – White

Telephone Nº: (01408) 621570
Fax Number: (01408) 621231
Ground Capacity: 4,000
Seating Capacity: 250
Pitch Size: 112 × 70 yards
Contact Address: Kevin Mackay, 2 Muirfield Road, Brora KW9 6QY
Contact Phone Nº: (01408) 621231

SCHOOL END

MAIN STAND

SEAFORTH ENCLOSURE

SOCIAL CLUB
CAR PARK

GENERAL INFORMATION
Supporters Club: c/o Club
Telephone Nº: (01408) 621570
Car Parking: Adjacent to the ground
Coach Parking: Adjacent to the ground
Nearest Railway Station: Brora
Nearest Bus Station: Brora
Club Shop: At the ground
Opening Times: Matchdays Only
Telephone Nº: (01408) 621231
Postal Sales: Yes
Nearest Police Station: Brora
Police Telephone Nº: (01408) 621222

GROUND INFORMATION
Away Supporters' Entrances & Sections:
No usual segregation

ADMISSION INFO (1999/2000 PRICES)
Adult Standing: £4.00
Adult Seating: £4.50
Child Standing: £2.00
Child Seating: £2.50
Programme Price: 50p

DISABLED INFORMATION
Wheelchairs: Accommodated
Helpers: Please phone the club for details
Prices: Please phone the club for details
Disabled Toilets: None
Are Bookings Necessary: Yes
Contact: (01408) 621231

Travelling Supporters' Information:
Routes: Take the A9 Northbound from Inverness and the Stadium is situated on the right upon entering the town. It is clearly visible from the road.

BUCKIE THISTLE FC

Founded: 1889	**Telephone N°:** (01542) 836468
Former Names: None	**Fax Number:** None
Nickname: 'The Jags'	**Pitch Size:** 109 × 73 yards
Ground: Victoria Park, Mid Mar Street,	**Ground Capacity:** 5,400
Buckie, Banffshire	**Seating Capacity:** 400
Record Attendance: 8,600 (1/3/58)	**Contact Address:** William Lobban
Colours: Shirts – Green and White Hoops	(Secretary), "Aig An Tigh", 4 Stripeside,
Shorts – White	Buckie AB56 1NP
	Contact Phone N°: (01542) 834433

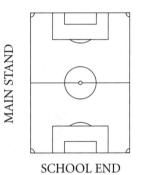

MAIN STAND

COVERED ENCLOSURE

SCHOOL END

GENERAL INFORMATION
Supporters Club: None
Telephone N°: –
Car Parking: Adjacent to the ground
Coach Parking: Adjacent to the ground
Nearest Railway Station: Keith (12 miles)
Nearest Bus Station: Buckie
Club Shop: None
Social Club: Buckie Thistle Social Club, 3/5 West Church Street, Buckie
Social Club Telephone N°: (01542) 832894
Nearest Police Station: Buckie
Police Telephone N°: (01542) 832222

GROUND INFORMATION
Away Supporters' Entrances & Sections:
No usual segregation

ADMISSION INFO (1999/2000 PRICES)
Adult Standing: £4.00
Adult Seating: £4.00
Concessions Standing: £2.00
Concessions Seating: £2.00
Programme Price: 50p

DISABLED INFORMATION
Wheelchairs: Accommodated when required, but no specific facilities
Helpers: Admitted
Prices: Normal prices apply
Disabled Toilets: None – but available within 100 yards of the ground
Are Bookings Necessary: No – but useful
Contact: (01542) 834433

Travelling Supporters' Information:
Routes: Take the A98 towards Cullen and turn left at Drybridge Crossroads for Buckie Town Centre. After ½ mile, turn left into West Cathcart Street, then left via South Pringle Street to Victoria Park. The ground is situated at the junction of South Pringle Street and Mid Mar Street.

CLACHNACUDDIN FC

Founded: 1886	**Telephone N°:** (01463) 238825
Former Names: None	**Ticket Information:** (01463) 710707
Nickname: 'Lilywhites'	**Fax Number:** (01463) 718261
Ground: Grant Street Park, Wyvis Place,	**Ground Capacity:** 3,000
Inverness IV3 6DR	**Seating Capacity:** 154
Record Attendance: 9,000 (27/8/51)	**Pitch Size:** 108 × 70 yards
Colours: Shirts – White	**Contact Address:** P. Corbett, c/o Club
Shorts – Black	**Contact Phone N°:** (01463) 710707

SOCIAL CLUB

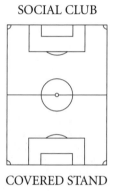

COVERED STAND

GENERAL INFORMATION

Supporters Club: None
Telephone N°: –
Car Parking: Adjacent to the ground
Coach Parking: Adjacent to the ground
Nearest Railway Station: Inverness
Nearest Bus Station: Inverness
Club Shop: At the ground
Opening Times: Matchdays Only
Telephone N°: (01463) 710707
Postal Sales: Yes
Nearest Police Station: Inverness
Police Telephone N°: (01463) 239191

GROUND INFORMATION

Away Supporters' Entrances & Sections:
No usual segregation

ADMISSION INFO (1999/2000 PRICES)

Adult Standing: £4.00
Adult Seating: £5.00
Child Standing: £2.00
Child Seating: £2.50
Programme Price: 20p

DISABLED INFORMATION

Wheelchairs: Accommodated
Helpers: Admitted
Prices: Normal prices apply
Disabled Toilets: Yes
Are Bookings Necessary: No
Contact: No

Travelling Supporters' Information:
Routes: From the East and South: From the roundabout at the junction of the A9 and A96, proceed into the Town Centre and over the River Ness. Turning right at the traffic lights (onto A862 to Dingwall) up Kenneth Street, over the roundabout onto Telford Street for 200 yards turning right into Telford Road opposite Fish Shop. At the top, turn left on Lower Kessack Street and left again. Left into Wyvis Place, ground is on the left.

COVE RANGERS FC

Founded: 1922
Former Names: None
Nickname: None
Ground: Allan Park, Loirston Road,
Cove, Aberdeen   AB12 4NS
Record Attendance: 2,300 (15/11/92)
Colours: Shirts – Blue
        Shorts – Blue

Telephone Nº: (01224) 871467 (Social Club)
Fax Number: (01224) 879023
Ground Capacity: 2,300
Seating Capacity: 200
Pitch Size: 104× 65 yards
Contact Address: Duncan Little, c/o Club
Contact Phone Nº: (01224) 890433 (Club)
Social Club Nº: (01224) 871467

GENERAL INFORMATION

Supporters Club: Brian Dean, c/o Social Club, Allan Park, Cove, Aberdeen
Telephone Nº: (01224) 871467
Car Parking: School Car Park/Loirston Road
Coach Parking: By Police Direction
Nearest Railway Station: Guild Street, Aberdeen
Nearest Bus Station: Guild Street, Aberdeen
Club Shop: At the Social Club
Opening Times: Matchdays Only
Telephone Nº: (01224) 871467
Postal Sales: Via Ian Armstrong, c/o Club
Nearest Police Station: Nigg Sub Station
Police Telephone Nº: (01224) 639111

GROUND INFORMATION

Away Supporters' Entrances & Sections:
Loirston Road entrances and accommodation

ADMISSION INFO (1999/2000 PRICES)

Adult Standing: £4.00
Adult Seating: £4.00
Child Standing: £2.00
Child Seating: £2.00
Programme Price: 50p

DISABLED INFORMATION

Wheelchairs: Accommodated
Helpers: Admitted
Prices: Normal prices apply
Disabled Toilets: Available in the Social Club
Are Bookings Necessary: No, but preferable
Contact: (01224) 890433 (Duncan Little)
(Matchdays);   (01224) 896282 (Evenings)

Travelling Supporters' Information:
Routes: From the North: Follow signs to Altens and Cove and take the Cove turn-off at the Skean Dhu Hotel roundabout along Loirston Road – Ground is ½ mile on the right; From the South: Take the Aberdeen Harbour turn-off some 10 miles north of Stonehaven and continue to Skean Dhu Hotel roundabout – then as North.
Bus Routes: No. 13 bus runs from City Centre to Ground.

DEVERONVALE FC

Founded: 1938
Former Names: None
Nickname: 'The Vale'
Ground: Princess Royal Park, Airlie Gardens, Banff   AB45 1HD
Record Attendance: 5,000 (27/4/52)
Colours: Shirts – Red with Black Trim
Shorts – White

Telephone Nº: (01261) 818489
Fax Number: (01261) 818489
Ground Capacity: 5,000
Seating Capacity: 300
Pitch Size: 109 × 78 yards
Contact Address: Stewart McPherson, 19 Reid Street, Banff   AB45 1HJ
Contact Phone Nº: (01261) 818489

BRIDGE STREET END

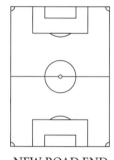

MAIN STAND

CANAL PARK BANK

NEW ROAD END

GENERAL INFORMATION
Supporters Club: The Secretary, c/o Club
Telephone Nº: (01261) 818489
Car Parking: Street Parking
Coach Parking: Bridge Road Car Park
Nearest Railway Station: Keith (20 miles)
Nearest Bus Station: Macduff (1 mile)
Club Shop: At the ground
Opening Times: Matchdays Only
Telephone Nº: (01261) 818489
Postal Sales: Yes
Nearest Police Station: Banff
Police Telephone Nº: (01261) 812555

GROUND INFORMATION
Away Supporters' Entrances & Sections:
No usual segregation

ADMISSION INFO (1999/2000 PRICES)
Adult Standing: £4.00
Adult Seating: £5.00
Child Standing: £2.00
Child Seating: £3.00
Programme Price: –

DISABLED INFORMATION
Wheelchairs: Accommodated
Helpers: Admitted
Prices: Please phone the club for details
Disabled Toilets: None
Are Bookings Necessary: Yes
Contact: (01261) 818489

Travelling Supporters' Information:
Routes: From Aberdeen: Take the first exit on the right after Banff Bridge – the ground is ½ mile on the left. From Inverness: Travel through Banff on the main by-pass and take the left turn before Banff Bridge – the ground is ½ mile on the left.

ELGIN CITY FC

Founded: 1893
Former Names: None
Nickname: 'Black and Whites'
Ground: Borough Briggs, Borough Briggs Road, Elgin   IV30 1AP
Record Attendance: 12,640 (17/2/68)
Pitch Size: 120 × 86 yards
Colours: Shirts – Black and White
Shorts – Black and Red

Telephone Nº: (01343) 547921
Ticket Information: (01343) 551114
Fax Number: (01343) 814133
Ground Capacity: 8,000
Seating Capacity: 450
Contact Address: J. Meichan, 30 Reidhaven Street, Elgin
Contact Phone Nº: (01343) 550850
Contact Fax Nº: (01343) 547921

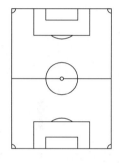

GENERAL INFORMATION

Supporters Club: Mrs. C. Jack, c/o Club
Telephone Nº: (01343) 545196
Car Parking: At the ground
Coach Parking: At the ground
Nearest Railway Station: Elgin (1 mile)
Nearest Bus Station: Elgin (¼ mile)
Club Shop: At the ground
Opening Times: Weekdays 8.30am to 5.30pm and also Saturdays 8.30am to 3.00pm
Telephone Nº: (01343) 551114
Postal Sales: Yes
Nearest Police Station: Elgin (1 mile)
Police Telephone Nº: (01343) 543101

GROUND INFORMATION

Away Supporters' Entrances & Sections:
West End entrances for the Covered Enclosure

ADMISSION INFO (1999/2000 PRICES)

Adult Standing: £4.00
Adult Seating: £5.00
Child Standing: £2.00
Child Seating: £2.50
Programme Price: 50p
Note: Admission is free for each under-16 if accompanied by a paying Adult.

DISABLED INFORMATION

Wheelchairs: Accommodated
Helpers: Admitted
Prices: Disabled admitted at concessionary prices
Disabled Toilets: Yes
Are Bookings Necessary: No
Contact: (01343) 550850 (J. Meichan, Secretary)

Travelling Supporters' Information:
Routes: Take the Alexandra bypass to the roundabout ½ mile from the City Centre and turn left towards Lossiemouth. Borough Briggs Road is on the left.

FORRES MECHANICS FC

Founded: 1884	**Ground Capacity**: 6,540
Former Names: None	**Seating Capacity**: 540
Nickname: 'Can Cans'	**Pitch Size**: 106 × 69 yards
Ground: Mosset Park, Lea Road, Forres IV36 0AU	**Contact Address**: C.C. Fraser, 19 Pilmuir Road West, Forres IV36 0HN
Record Attendance: 7,000 (2/2/57)	**Contact Phone Nº**: (01309) 672349
Colours: Shirts – Chocolate and Gold	**OR Contact**: Moray G. Cattenach,
Shorts – Gold	8 St. Margaret's Court, Forres
Telephone/Fax Number: (01309) 675096	**Telephone Nº**: (01309) 676993

BOGTON END

CAR PARK STAND

GAS WORKS END

GENERAL INFORMATION
Supporters Club: Paul Wilson, 141c High Street, Forres
Telephone Nº: (01309) 675784
Car Parking: At the ground
Coach Parking: At the ground
Nearest Railway Station: Forres
Nearest Bus Station: Forres
Club Shop: At the ground
Opening Times: Matchdays only
Telephone Nº: (01309) 675096
Postal Sales: –
Nearest Police Station: Forres
Police Telephone Nº: (01309) 672224

GROUND INFORMATION
Away Supporters' Entrances & Sections:
No usual segregation

ADMISSION INFO (1999/2000 PRICES)
Adult Standing: £4.00
Adult Seating: £5.00
Child/O.A.P. Standing: £2.00
Child/O.A.P. Seating: £3.00
Programme Price: 50p

DISABLED INFORMATION
Wheelchairs: Accommodated
Helpers: Admitted
Prices: Normal prices apply
Disabled Toilets: One available
Are Bookings Necessary: No
Contact: (01309) 675096

Travelling Supporters' Information:
Routes: Exit the Forres Bypass (A940) for Grantown on Spey/Forres Town Centre. Take the first left along the burn, cross the bridge then first left for the ground. The Stand is clearly visible from the Bypass.

FORT WILLIAM FC

Founded: 1984
Former Names: None
Nickname: 'The Fort'
Ground: Claggan Park, Fort William, Inverness-shire
Record Attendance: 1,500 (4/1/86)
Colours: Shirts – Gold and Black
Shorts – Black
Telephone Nº: None at the ground

Ground Capacity: 4,600
Seating Capacity: 400
Pitch Size: 102 × 80 yards
Contact Address: J. Baird, 11 Clerk Drive, Corpach, Fort William   PH33 6LZ
Contact Phone Nº: (01397) 708000
Contact Fax Number: (01397) 705627
Social Club Number: (01397) 703829

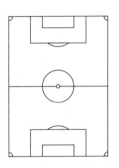

STAND

GENERAL INFORMATION
Supporters Club: None
Telephone Nº: –
Car Parking: At the ground
Coach Parking: At the ground
Nearest Railway Station: Fort William
Nearest Bus Station: Fort William
Club Shop: None
Opening Times: –
Telephone Nº: –
Postal Sales: –
Nearest Police Station: High Street, Fort William
Police Telephone Nº: (01397) 702361

GROUND INFORMATION
Away Supporters' Entrances & Sections:
No usual segregation

ADMISSION INFO (1999/2000 PRICES)
Adult Standing: £4.00
Adult Seating: £4.00
Child Standing: £2.00
Child Seating: £2.00
Programme Price: None

DISABLED INFORMATION
Wheelchairs: Accommodated
Helpers: Please phone the club for details
Prices: Please phone the club for details
Disabled Toilets: None
Are Bookings Necessary: No
Contact: (01397) 708000

Travelling Supporters' Information:
Routes: From the South: Approaching Fort William on the A82, proceed on the Bypass of the Town Centre. After 2 roundabouts continue on Belford Road past the Railway Station on the left and the Swimming Baths on the right. After ½ mile and crossing over the River Nevis, take the first right into Claggan Road and the ground is ½ mile on the left.

FRASERBURGH FC

Founded: 1910	**Telephone Nº:** (01346) 518444
Former Names: None	**Fax Number:** (01346) 511822
Nickname: 'The Broch'	**Ground Capacity:** 4,500
Ground: Bellslea Park, Seaforth Street,	**Seating Capacity:** 480
Fraserburgh AB43 9BD	**Pitch Size:** 106 × 66 yards
Record Attendance: 5,800 (13/2/54)	**Contact Address:** Finlay Noble,
Colours: Shirts – Black and White Stripes	18 Bawdley Head, Fraserburgh AB43 9SE
Shorts – Black	**Contact Phone Nº:** (01346) 518444

GENERAL INFORMATION
Supporters Club: David Henderson, 3 Lewis Place, Fraserburgh AB43 9WU
Telephone Nº: (01346) 516693
Car Parking: At the ground
Coach Parking: At the ground
Nearest Railway Station: Aberdeen (40 miles)
Nearest Bus Station: Fraserburgh
Club Shop: At the ground
Opening Times: Matchdays Only
Telephone Nº: (01346) 518444
Postal Sales: Yes
Web site: www.burghfc.demon.co.uk
Nearest Police Station: Fraserburgh
Police Telephone Nº: (01346) 513121

GROUND INFORMATION
Away Supporters' Entrances & Sections:
No usual segregation

ADMISSION INFO (1999/2000 PRICES)
Adult Standing: £4.00
Adult Seating: £4.50
Child Standing: £2.00
Child Seating: £2.50
Programme Price: £1.00

DISABLED INFORMATION
Wheelchairs: Accommodated
Helpers: Admitted
Prices: Normal prices apply
Disabled Toilets: Yes
Are Bookings Necessary: No
Contact: (01346) 518444

Web site: www.burghfc.demon.co.uk

Travelling Supporters' Information:
Routes: The ground is situated in the Town Centre, off Seaforth Street.

HUNTLY FC

Founded: 1928
Former Names: None
Nickname: None
Ground: Christie Park, East Park Street, Huntly, Aberdeenshire AB54 8JE
Record Attendance: 4,500 (18/2/95)
Colours: Shirts – Black and Gold
Shorts – Black

Telephone Nº: (01466) 793548
Fax Number: None
Ground Capacity: 4,500
Seating Capacity: 270
Pitch Size: 105 × 72 yards
Contact Address: Peter Morrison, Glenlea, Littlejohn Street, Huntly AB54 8HL
Contact Phone Nº: (01466) 793269

EAST PARK STREET

GENERAL INFORMATION
Social Club: Within the ground
Telephone Nº: (01466) 793680
Car Parking: At the ground
Coach Parking: At the ground
Nearest Railway Station: Huntly (1 mile)
Nearest Bus Station: Huntly (¼ mile)
Club Shop: At the ground
Opening Times: Matchdays Only
Telephone Nº: –   **Postal Sales:** –
Web site: www.huntlyfc.co.uk
Nearest Police Station: Adjacent to the ground
Police Telephone Nº: (01466) 792246

GROUND INFORMATION
Away Supporters' Entrances & Sections:
No usual segregation

ADMISSION INFO (1999/2000 PRICES)
Adult Standing: £4.00
Adult Seating: £5.00
Child Standing: £2.50
Child Seating: £3.50
Programme Price: £1.00

DISABLED INFORMATION
Wheelchairs: Accommodated
Helpers: Please phone the club for details
Prices: Please phone the club for details
Disabled Toilets: None
Are Bookings Necessary: No
Contact: (01466) 793269

Web site: www.huntlyfc.co.uk

Travelling Supporters' Information:
Routes: Enter the Town off the A96 and proceed along King George V Avenue and Gordon Street. Pass through the Town Centre Square, along Castle Street to East Park Street and the ground is on the right before the Castle.

KEITH FC

Founded: 1919	**Telephone Nº**: (01542) 887407 (matchdays)
Former Names: None	**Fax Number**: (01542) 882629
Nickname: 'Maroons'	**Ground Capacity**: 5,500
Ground: Kynoch Park, Balloch Road,	**Seating Capacity**: 450
Keith AB55 5EN	**Pitch Size**: 110 × 75 yards
Record Attendance: 5,820 (4/2/28)	**Correspondence Address**: Alex Rutherford,
Colours: Shirts – Maroon with Sky Blue	c/o Club
Shorts – Maroon with Sky Blue	**Contact Phone Nº**: (01542) 886644

GENERAL INFORMATION

Supporters Club: None
Telephone Nº: –
Car Parking: Street parking in Balloch Road, Moss Street and Reidhaven Square
Coach Parking: Balloch Road or Bridge Street Coach Park
Nearest Railway Station: Keith (1 mile)
Nearest Bus Station: Keith
Club Shop: At the ground
Opening Times: Weekdays 9.00am to 4.00pm
Telephone Nº: (01542) 882629
Postal Sales: Yes
Nearest Police Station: Turner Street, Keith
Police Telephone Nº: (01542) 882502

GROUND INFORMATION

Away Supporters' Entrances & Sections:
No usual segregation except for some Cup Ties

ADMISSION INFO (1999/2000 PRICES)

Adult Standing: £4.00
Adult Seating: £5.00
Child Standing: £2.00
Child Seating: £3.00
Programme Price: 50p

DISABLED INFORMATION

Wheelchairs: Accommodated
Helpers: Admitted
Prices: Normal prices apply
Disabled Toilets: None
Are Bookings Necessary: Yes
Contact: (01542) 886644

Travelling Supporters' Information:
Routes: From Aberdeen: Coming in on the A96, turn right up Bridge Street (across from the Bus Stop at Reidhaven Square), then take the first left for Balloch Road; From Inverness: Coming in on the A96, turn second left after the Citroen Keith Garage in Moss Street onto Balloch Road.

LOSSIEMOUTH FC

Founded: 1945
Former Names: None
Nickname: 'Coasters'
Ground: Grant Park, Kellas Avenue, Lossiemouth IV31 6JG
Record Attendance: 2,700 (28/12/48)
Pitch Size: 110 × 60 yards
Colours: Shirts – Red
　　　　　　Shorts – Red

Telephone Nº: (01343) 813717
Fax Number: (01343) 815440
Social Club Nº: (01343) 813168
Ground Capacity: 3,500
Seating Capacity: 250
Contact Address: Alan McIntosh, 3 Forties Place, Lossiemouth IV31 6SS
Contact Phone Nº: (01343) 813328 and (07967) 579384

GENERAL INFORMATION

Supporters Club: Neil MacPherson, 39-41 MacDuff Street, Lossiemouth
Telephone Nº: (01343) 813168
Car Parking: At the ground
Coach Parking: At the ground
Nearest Railway Station: Elgin
Nearest Bus Station: Lossiemouth
Club Shop: At the ground
Opening Times: Matchdays Only
Telephone Nº: (01343) 813739
Postal Sales: Yes
Nearest Police Station: Lossiemouth
Police Telephone Nº: (01343) 812022

GROUND INFORMATION

Away Supporters' Entrances & Sections:
No usual segregation

ADMISSION INFO (1999/2000 PRICES)

Adult Standing: £4.00
Adult Seating: £4.00
Child Standing: £2.00
Child Seating: £2.00
Programme Price: 50p

DISABLED INFORMATION

Wheelchairs: Accommodated
Helpers: Admitted
Prices: Free of charge for the disabled
Disabled Toilets: Yes
Are Bookings Necessary: Yes
Contact: (01343) 813328 (Alan McIntosh)

Travelling Supporters' Information:
Routes: Take the Main Road into Lossiemouth and take the second turning on the right. Turn right again after 100 yards.

NAIRN COUNTY FC

Founded: 1914	**Telephone Nº:** (01667) 454298
Former Names: None	**Fax Number:** (01667) 462510
Nickname: 'The Wee County'	**Ground Capacity:** 3,800
Ground: Station Park, Balblair Road,	**Seating Capacity:** 250
Nairn IV12 5LT	**Pitch Size:** 110 × 62 yards
Record Attendance: 4,000 (2/9/50)	**Contact Address:** John McNeill, 50 Station
Colours: Shirts – Yellow and Black	Road, Ardersier, Inverness IV2 7ST
Shorts – Yellow	**Contact Phone Nº:** (01667) 462510

GENERAL INFORMATION
Supporters Club: Nairn County Social Club
Telephone Nº: (01667) 451504
Car Parking: At the ground
Coach Parking: At the ground
Nearest Railway Station: Nairn (adjacent)
Nearest Bus Station: King Street, Nairn (½ mile)
Club Shop: At the Social Club
Opening Times: Club Hours only
Telephone Nº: (01667) 453286
Postal Sales: Alex MacKintosh, c/o Social Club
Nearest Police Station: King Street, Nairn
Police Telephone Nº: (01667) 452222

GROUND INFORMATION
Away Supporters' Entrances & Sections:
No usual segregation

ADMISSION INFO (1999/2000 PRICES)
Adult Standing: £4.00
Adult Seating: £5.00
Child Standing: £2.00
Child Seating: £2.50
Programme Price: £1.00

DISABLED INFORMATION
Wheelchairs: Accommodated in the Stand
Helpers: Admitted
Prices: £4.00 for the disabled
Disabled Toilets: None
Are Bookings Necessary: No
Contact: (01667) 462510 (John McNeill)

Travelling Supporters' Information:
Routes: The ground is situated on the south side of Nairn at the bottom of the Main Street, adjacent to the Railway Station.

PETERHEAD FC

Founded: 1891	**Telephone N°:** (01779) 478256
Former Names: None	**Fax Number:** (01779) 475075
Nickname: 'Blue Toon'	**Ground Capacity:** 4,000
Ground: Balmoor Stadium, Peterhead AB42 6HG	**Seating Capacity:** 470
	Pitch Size: 110 × 74 yards
Record Attendance: Not known	**Contact Address:** G. Ritchie, 18 Skelton Street, Peterhead
Colours: Shirts – Royal Blue + White Sleeves Shorts – White	**Contact Phone N°:** (01779) 473434

GENERAL INFORMATION

Supporters Club: None
Telephone N°: –
Car Parking: At the ground
Coach Parking: At the ground
Nearest Railway Station: Aberdeen
Nearest Bus Station: Peterhead
Club Shop: None
Opening Times: –
Telephone N°: –
Postal Sales: –
Nearest Police Station: Peterhead
Police Telephone N°: (01779) 472571

GROUND INFORMATION

Away Supporters' Entrances & Sections:
No usual segregation

ADMISSION INFO (1999/2000 PRICES)

Adult Standing: £4.00
Adult Seating: £4.50
Child Standing: £2.00
Child Seating: £2.00
Programme Price: 50p

DISABLED INFORMATION

Wheelchairs: Accommodated
Helpers: Please phone the club for details
Prices: Please phone the club for details
Disabled Toilets: Yes
Are Bookings Necessary: Yes
Contact: (01779) 473434

Travelling Supporters' Information:
Routes: The ground is situated on the left of the main road from Fraserburgh (A952), about 300 yards past the swimming pool.

ROTHES FC

Founded: 1938	**Telephone N°:** (01340) 831972
Former Names: Rothes Victoria FC	**Social Club N°:** (01340) 831348
Nickname: 'The Speysiders'	**Fax Number:** None
Ground: Mackessack Park, Rothes, AB38	**Ground Capacity:** 2,650
Record Attendance: 2,054 (September 1946)	**Seating Capacity:** 160
Pitch Size: 108 × 74 yards	**Contact Address:** Neil R. McKenzie, c/o
Colours: Shirts – Tangerine	Rothes FC Social Club, Seafield Square, Rothes
Shorts – Black	**Contact Phone N°:** (01340) 831344

GENERAL INFORMATION

Supporters Club: None
Telephone N°: –
Car Parking: At the ground
Coach Parking: At the ground
Nearest Railway Station: Elgin
Nearest Bus Station: Elgin
Club Shop: None
Opening Times: –
Telephone N°: –
Postal Sales: –
Nearest Police Station: Rothes
Police Telephone N°: (01340) 831341

GROUND INFORMATION

Away Supporters' Entrances & Sections:
No usual segregation

ADMISSION INFO (1999/2000 PRICES)

Adult Standing: £4.00
Adult Seating: £5.00
Child Standing: £2.00
Child Seating: £2.50
Programme Price: None

DISABLED INFORMATION

Wheelchairs: Accommodated
Helpers: Admitted
Prices: Normal prices apply
Disabled Toilets: None
Are Bookings Necessary: No
Contact: (01340) 831344 (Secretary)

Travelling Supporters' Information:
Routes: The ground is situated by Grant's Whisky Distillery at the North side of Rothes, by the junction of the Keith and Elgin Roads.

WICK ACADEMY FC

Founded: 1893
Former Names: None
Nickname: 'The Scorries'
Ground: Harmsworth Park, South Road, Wick, Caithness KW1 5NH
Record Attendance: 2,000 (30/7/84)
Colours: Shirts – Black and White Stripes
  Shorts – Black

Telephone Nº: (01955) 602446
Fax Number: (01955) 602446
Ground Capacity: 2,000
Seating Capacity: 433
Pitch Size: 106 × 76 yards
Contact Address: Mr. A. Carter, 8 Argyle Square, Wick, Caithness KW1 5AL
Contact Phone Nº: (01955) 604275

GENERAL INFORMATION
Supporters Club: None
Telephone Nº: –
Car Parking: At the ground
Coach Parking: At the ground
Nearest Railway Station: Wick (10 minutes walk)
Nearest Bus Station: Wick
Club Shop: Wick Sports Shop, High Street, Wick
Opening Times: 9.00am to 5.00pm
Telephone Nº: (01955) 602930
Postal Sales: Yes
Nearest Police Station: Bridge Street, Wick
Police Telephone Nº: (01955) 603551

GROUND INFORMATION
Away Supporters' Entrances & Sections:
No usual segregation

ADMISSION INFO (1999/2000 PRICES)
Adult Standing: £4.00
Adult Seating: £5.00 (North Stand)
Child Standing: £2.00
Child Seating: £3.00 (North Stand)
Programme Price: 50p

DISABLED INFORMATION
Wheelchairs: 2 spaces available in the North Stand
Helpers: Please phone the club for details
Prices: Please phone the club for details
Disabled Toilets: None
Are Bookings Necessary: No
Contact: (01955) 604275

Travelling Supporters' Information:
Routes: The ground is situated on the A9 road from Inverness beside the Cemetery.

Press & Journal Highland League Season 1998/99	Brora Rangers	Buckie Thistle	Clachnacuddin	Cove Rangers	Deveronvale	Elgin City	Forres Mechanics	Fort William	Fraserburgh	Huntly	Keith	Lossiemouth	Nairn County	Peterhead	Rothes	Wick Academy
Brora Rangers		0-0	0-1	3-1	1-2	2-5	0-1	3-1	2-2	2-3	1-4	3-2	4-2	1-5	6-0	1-0
Buckie Thistle	0-2		0-3	1-4	2-0	1-0	0-3	0-0	1-4	1-3	0-2	4-0	2-0	0-2	2-2	2-1
Clachnacuddin	1-0	1-0		2-3	2-2	3-1	4-1	5-1	3-1	1-2	2-2	3-0	3-2	1-2	2-2	7-1
Cove Rangers	5-4	6-1	1-1		7-2	1-2	2-0	10-0	1-2	1-3	2-2	1-0	3-0	1-2	3-0	5-0
Deveronvale	2-0	2-5	3-4	3-3		1-2	3-2	4-2	0-1	2-5	0-3	1-2	2-2	0-4	2-0	2-0
Elgin City	5-1	4-3	1-0	4-2	5-0		2-1	5-0	1-0	0-2	2-1	1-0	1-0	0-5	1-0	4-2
Forres Mechs.	3-3	1-4	2-2	1-1	1-0	1-3		4-2	1-1	2-1	2-3	4-1	10-2	0-1	3-2	4-1
Fort William	0-7	0-2	2-4	1-7	2-3	0-3	1-2		0-5	0-8	1-3	3-0	1-2	0-5	1-4	0-1
Fraserburgh	5-2	3-0	1-1	2-1	5-1	3-2	4-0	9-0		3-3	3-4	3-2	3-0	1-3	3-1	5-0
Huntly	0-3	3-0	4-3	5-2	2-1	2-0	3-2	2-0	2-1		5-1	2-0	4-0	1-1	1-0	5-1
Keith	3-1	2-1	3-3	2-0	1-3	3-2	1-0	6-0	3-2	3-2		3-1	6-0	2-1	1-0	3-0
Lossiemouth	1-1	1-0	0-4	1-2	1-1	0-4	2-2	3-1	2-2	2-3	4-2		4-1	1-5	2-1	1-2
Nairn County	2-2	3-1	0-6	0-5	1-5	1-7	1-5	5-2	1-4	1-5	1-8	1-2		0-3	0-2	2-5
Peterhead	4-0	4-0	4-1	2-3	3-0	2-0	5-1	7-1	1-1	1-1	1-1	3-0	4-1		1-0	4-0
Rothes	1-3	1-1	2-3	1-1	5-6	1-3	1-1	5-1	0-5	3-1	1-7	2-1	3-0	1-3		3-0
Wick Academy	0-3	3-2	2-2	1-4	0-3	1-1	4-0	3-1	0-3	1-3	0-7	2-4	2-1	0-1	0-2	

Highland Football League

Season 1998/99

Peterhead	30	24	4	2	89	19	76
Huntly	30	23	3	4	86	38	72
Keith	30	22	4	4	92	41	70
Elgin City	30	21	1	8	71	39	64
Fraserburgh	30	18	6	6	86	39	60
Clachnacuddin	30	16	8	6	80	45	56
Cove Rangers	30	16	5	9	88	48	53
Forres Mechanics	30	11	6	13	60	60	39
Brora Rangers	30	11	5	14	61	63	38
Deveronvale	30	11	4	15	57	72	37
Rothes	30	8	5	17	46	64	29
Buckie Thistle	30	8	4	18	36	60	28
Lossiemouth	30	8	4	18	40	67	28
Wick Academy	30	7	2	21	33	85	23
Nairn County	30	3	2	25	32	114	11
Fort William	30	1	1	28	24	127	4

Champions: Peterhead

76

THE EAST OF SCOTLAND LEAGUE

Founded
1930

Secretary
Mr. J.M. Greenhorn

Address
2 Baberton Mains Court,
Edinburgh   EH14 3ER

Phone
(0131) 442-1402

ANNAN ATHLETIC FC

1999/2000 Season: Premier Division
Year Founded: 1942
Nickname: None
Former Names: Solway Star FC
Ground: Galabank, North Street,
Annan, Dumfries & Galloway
Ground Phone Nº: (01461) 204108

Ground Capacity: 2,000
Seating Capacity: None
Colours: Black and Gold vertical striped
shirts with Black shorts
Contact Address: A. Irving, Secretary,
1 Newlands Rise, Annan   DG12 5HT
Contact Phone Nº: (01461) 203702

CIVIL SERVICE STROLLERS FC

1999/2000 Season: Premier Division
Year Founded: 1908
Nickname: 'Strollers'
Former Names: None
Ground: Muirhouse Sports Ground,
Marine Drive, Edinburgh
Ground Phone Nº: (0131) 332-0650

Ground Capacity: 500 approximately
Seating Capacity: None
Colours: Shirts are white with a dark
blue stripe and blue shorts are worn
Contact Address: W. Christie,
50 Craigleith Hill Avenue, Edinburgh
Contact Phone Nº: (0131) 332-3567

CRAIGROYSTON FC

1999/2000 Season: Premier Division
Year Founded: 1976
Nickname: 'Craigie'
Former Names: None
Ground Address: City Park, Ferry Road,
Edinburgh
Ground Phone Nº: None

Ground Capacity: –
Seating Capacity: –
Colours: Yellow shirts with blue shorts
Contact Address: J. Murray, 60 Ratcliffe
Terrace, Edinburgh   EH9 1QU
Contact Phone Nº: (0131) 668-2188
(home); (0131) 667-9923 (Business)

EASTHOUSES LILY MINERS WELFARE FC

1999/2000 Season: Premier Division
Year Founded: 1969
Nickname: 'The Lily'
Former Names: None
Ground: Newbattle Complex, Easthouses,
Dalkeith
Ground Phone Nº: (0131) 663-9768

Ground Capacity: 1,500
Seating Capacity: None
Colours: Red shirts with white shorts
Contact Address: R. Paul, 90 Langlaw
Road, Mayfield, Dalkeith   EH22 5AS
Contact Phone Nº: (0131) 663-9768

EDINBURGH CITY FC

1999/2000 Season: Premier Division
Year Founded: 1928 (Re-formed 1986)
Nickname: 'The City'
Former Names: None
Ground: Meadowbank Stadium, London Road, Edinburgh   EH7 6AE
Ground Phone N°: (0131) 661-5351

Ground Capacity: 13,841
Seating Capacity: 13,841
Colours: White shirts and black shorts
Contact Address: D. Baxter, 23 South Elixa Place, Edinburgh   EH8 7PG
Contact Phone N°: (0131) 652-1633 (home); (0131) 244-6577 (business)

LOTHIAN THISTLE FC

1999/2000 Season: Premier Division
Year Founded: 1969
Nickname: 'Thistle'
Former Names: None
Ground: Campbell Park, Saughton Enclosure, Edinburgh
Ground Phone N°: –

Ground Capacity: 1,000
Seating Capacity: –
Colours: Blue shirts and white shorts
Contact Address: Tom Allison, 31 Clermiston Place, Edinburgh   EH4 7DN
Contact Phone N°: (0131) 336-1751 (home); (0131) 333-1976 (business)

PEEBLES ROVERS FC

1999/2000 Season: Premier Division
Year Founded: 1894
Nickname: 'The Rovers'
Former Names: None
Ground: Whitestone Park, Peebles
Ground Phone N°: –

Ground Capacity: 3,000
Seating Capacity: 500
Colours: Red and white shirts and shorts
Contact Address: C. Morrish, 8 Springhill Road, Peebles   EH45 9EW
Contact Phone N°: (01721) 720543

THE SPARTANS FC

1999/2000 Season: Premier Division
Year Founded: 1951
Nickname: None
Former Names: None
Ground: City Park, Ferry Road, Edinburgh
Ground Phone N°: –

Ground Capacity: 3,000
Seating Capacity: –
Colours: White shirts and red shorts
Contact Address: J. McCabe, 72 Denholm Road, Musselburgh   EH21 6TU
Contact Phone N°: (0131) 665-8225 (home); (0131) 621-8322 (business)

VALE OF LEITHEN FC

1999/2000 Season: Premier Division	**Ground Phone Nº:** None
Year Founded: 1891	**Colours:** Navy shirts with white sleeves and navy shorts
Nickname: 'Vale'	
Former Names: None	**Contact Address:** I. Haggarty, 11 Peebles
Ground: Victoria Park, Innerleithen	Road, Innerleithen EH44 6QX
Ground Capacity: 1,500	**Contact Phone Nº:** (01896) 830995
Seating Capacity: None	(home); (0131) 244-2524 (business)

WHITEHILL WELFARE FC

1999/2000 Season: Premier Division	**Seating Capacity:** None
Year Founded: 1953	**Colours:** Maroon and sky blue shirts with white shorts
Nickname: 'The Welfare'	
Ground: Ferguson Park, Carnethie Street, Rosewell, Midlothian	**Contact Address:** Peter McGauley, 47 Prestonhall Crescent, Rosewell, Midlothian EH24 9BQ
Ground Phone Nº: (0131) 440-0115	
Ground Capacity: 4,000	**Contact Phone Nº:** (0131) 440-3417

East of Scotland League Premier Division Season 1998/99	Annan Athletic	Civil Service Stroll.	Craigroyston	Edinburgh City	Lothian Thistle	Peebles Rovers	Pencaitland	Spartans	Tollcross United	Whitehill Welfare
Annan Athletic		2-1	2-1	1-0	1-1	4-1	4-2	2-1	3-2	2-3
Civil Serv. Stroll.	2-3		3-1	0-4	2-1	2-1	3-1	0-2	0-1	0-5
Craigroyston	2-3	3-4		2-2	1-3	3-2	2-1	1-3	2-2	0-2
Edinburgh City	1-1	0-1	1-0		0-4	1-0	1-1	0-3	3-2	1-2
Lothian Thistle	1-1	1-3	2-2	3-3		5-2	0-2	1-1	2-0	1-2
Peebles Rovers	2-1	2-2	1-4	1-1	2-2		1-1	1-5	0-0	1-1
Pencaitland	0-1	3-3	0-2	0-1	1-3	0-6		0-1	1-0	0-4
Spartans	2-2	2-1	4-1	2-1	2-1	3-2	5-1		2-0	0-0
Tollcross United	1-4	1-2	0-1	1-2	0-0	2-3	1-0	0-2		1-2
Whitehill Welfare	3-2	1-2	4-1	2-1	3-1	1-0	3-0	2-2	3-0	

East of Scotland League
Premier Division Season 1998/99

Whitehill Welfare	18	14	3	1	43	15	45
Spartans	18	13	4	1	42	16	43
Annan Athletic	18	11	4	3	39	26	37
Civil Service Strollers	18	9	2	7	31	34	29
Edinburgh City	18	6	5	7	23	26	23
Lothian Thistle	18	5	7	6	32	28	22
Craigroyston	18	5	3	10	29	39	18
Peebles Rovers	18	3	6	9	28	38	15
Tollcross United	18	2	3	13	14	32	9
Pencaitland	18	2	3	13	14	41	9

Champions: Whitehill Welfare

Relegated: Pencaitland & Tollcross United

COLDSTREAM FC

1999/2000 Season: First Division
Year Founded: 1895
Nickname: 'The Streamers'
Former Names: None
Ground: Home Park, Coldstream, Berwickshire
Ground Phone Nº: (01890) 883085

Ground Capacity: –
Seating Capacity: –
Colours: Royal blue shirts with blue shorts
Contact Address: Rose Purvis, 3 Luke's Brae, Coldstream   TD12 4BT
Contact Phone Nº: (01890) 882912

EDINBURGH ATHLETIC FC

1999/2000 Season: First Division
Year Founded: 1968
Nickname: 'The Crew'
Former Names: Manor Thistle FC
Ground: Muirhouse Sports Ground, Marine Drive, Edinburgh
Ground Phone Nº: (0131) 332-0650

Ground Capacity: 500 approximately
Seating Capacity: –
Colours: Shirts are maroon with sky blue trim and the shorts are white
Contact Address: Mr. I. Gracie, 1 The Glebe, East Saltoun, East Lothian
Contact Phone Nº: (01875) 340983

EDINBURGH UNIVERSITY FC

1999/2000 Season: First Division
Year Founded: 1878
Nickname: 'The Burgh'
Ground: Peffermill Playing Fields, Peffermill Road, Edinburgh
Ground Phone Nº: (0131) 667-7541
Colours: Green shirts and blue shorts

Ground Capacity: 212
Seating Capacity: 12
Contact Address: C. Hewitt, Edinburgh University Sports Union, 48 Pleasance, Edinburgh   EH8 9TJ
Contact Phone Nº: (0131) 650-2346 or (0131) 650-2347

EYEMOUTH UNITED FC

1999/2000 Season: First Division
Year Founded: 1948
Nickname: 'The Fishermen'
Former Names: None
Ground: Gunsgreen Park, Johns Road, Eyemouth, Berwickshire
Ground Phone Nº: None

Ground Capacity: –
Seating Capacity: –
Colours: Maroon shirts and white shorts
Contact Address: John Windram, 'Kintyre', Upper Houndlaw, Eyemouth, Berwickshire   TD14 5BU
Contact Phone Nº: (01890) 750601

Gala Fairydean FC

1999/2000 Season: First Division
Year Founded: 1907
Nickname: 'The Dean'
Former Names: None
Ground: Netherdale, Galashiels
Ground Phone Nº: (01896) 753554

Ground Capacity: 5,500
Seating Capacity: 495
Colours: Black & white shirts and shorts
Contact Address: George McGill,
25 Melrose Road, Galashiels   TD1 2AT
Contact Phone Nº: (01896) 754500
(home); (0831) 575825 (mobile)

Hawick Royal Albert FC

1999/2000 Season: First Division
Year Founded: 1947
Nickname: 'The Albert'
Former Names: None
Ground: Albert Park, Mansfield Road,
Hawick
Ground Phone Nº: (01450) 374231

Ground Capacity: 2,000
Seating Capacity: 500
Colours: Royal blue shirts and shorts
Contact Address: J. Batten, 34b Chay
Blyth Place, Hawick   TD9 8HY
Contact Phone Nº: (01450) 377447

Heriot-Watt University FC

1999/2000 Season: First Division
Year Founded: 1942
Nickname: 'The Watt'
Ground: Heriot-Watt University
Riccarton Campus, Riccarton, Edinburgh
Ground Phone Nº: (0131) 449-5111
Ground Capacity: 1,800

Seating Capacity: –
Colours: Blue and yellow shirts with blue
shorts
Contact Address: R. Silander,
13 Craiglockhart Grove, Edinburgh
EH14 1ET
Contact Phone Nº: (0131) 443-1913

Kelso United FC

1999/2000 Season: First Division
Year Founded: 1924
Nickname: 'Tweedsiders'
Former Names: None
Ground: Woodside Park, Kelso,
Roxburghshire
Ground Phone Nº: (01573) 223780

Ground Capacity: 1,000
Seating Capacity: None
Colours: Black and white striped shirts
with black shorts
Contact Address: A.H. Douglas,
34 Dyers Court, Kelso   TD5 7NQ
Contact Phone Nº: (01573) 225314

PENCAITLAND & ORMISTON FC

1999/2000 Season: First Division
Year Founded: 1884
Former Names: Pencaitland Amateur FC
Ground: Recreation Park, Ormiston, East Lothian
Ground Capacity: 1,000
Seating Capacity: None

Colours: Maroon and white shirts with white shorts
Contact Address: J.M. Greenohorn, 2 Baberton Mains Court, Edinburgh EH14 3ER
Contact Phone Nº: (0131) 538-0289 (home); (0131) 656-5032 (business)

PRESTON ATHLETIC FC

1999/2000 Season: First Division
Year Founded: 1945
Nickname: 'Panners'
Ground: Pennypit Park, Rope Walk, Prestonpans, East Lothian
Ground Capacity: 4,000
Seating Capacity: 313

Colours: Shirts are navy blue with red and white trim and shorts are navy blue
Contact Address: R. McNeill, 25 West Windygoul Gardens, Tranent EH33 2LB
Contact Phone Nº: (01875) 611830 (home); (0131) 272-4000 (business)

SELKIRK FC

1999/2000 Season: First Division
Year Founded: 1880
Nickname: 'Souters'
Former Names: None
Ground: Ettrick Park, Riverside Road, Selkirk, Selkirkshire
Ground Phone Nº: (01750) 20478

Ground Capacity: 3,000
Seating Capacity: None
Colours: Shirts and shorts are Royal blue with white trim
Contact Address: D. Kerr, 17 Kilncroft, Selkirk
Contact Phone Nº: (01750) 23060

THREAVE ROVERS FC

1999/2000 Season: First Division
Year Founded: 1953
Nickname: 'Rovers'
Former Names: None
Ground: Meadow Park, Castle Douglas, Dumfries & Galloway
Ground Phone Nº: (01556) 504536

Ground Capacity: 1,500
Seating Capacity: None
Colours: Black and white striped shirts with black shorts
Contact Address: D. McLean, 278 King Street, Castle Douglas DG7 1HA
Contact Phone Nº: (01556) 503185

TOLLCROSS UNITED FC

1999/2000 Season: First Division **Year Founded**: 1971 **Nickname**: 'The Cross' **Ground**: Fernieside Recreation Park, Fernieside Avenue, Edinburgh **Ground Capacity**: 400 **Seating Capacity**: None	**Colours**: Red shirts with white sleeves and white shorts **Contact Address**: Alistair Wilkie, 3/1 Rankin Avenue, Edinburgh EH9 3DD **Contact Phone Nº**: (0131) 621-1148 (home); (0131) 467-5555 (business)

East of Scotland League First Division Season 1998/99

	Coldstream	Easthouses Lily	Edinburgh Athletic	Edinburgh Univ.	Eyemouth United	Gala Fairydean	Hawick Royal Alb.	Heriot-Watt Univ.	Kelso United	Preston Athletic	Selkirk	Threave Rovers	Vale of Leithen
Coldstream	■	1-1	8-1	2-1	3-0	3-0	0-0	0-0	4-1	0-4	4-1	3-1	3-2
Easthouses Lily	1-0	■	1-0	2-0	3-1	1-1	2-2	1-0	5-0	0-0	2-1	1-1	1-3
Edinburgh Ath.	0-2	1-1	■	2-3	1-1	0-5	3-2	2-1	0-1	1-3	1-2	1-5	2-5
Edinburgh Univ.	2-2	0-0	1-2	■	3-3	2-1	1-1	3-1	2-1	0-4	2-5	1-1	4-2
Eyemouth United	1-3	0-2	0-0	0-3	■	0-2	3-5	1-3	2-1	2-2	1-1	1-2	0-5
Gala Fairydean	4-2	1-4	1-0	0-0	4-1	■	0-1	1-0	1-0	0-2	4-0	3-5	1-2
Hawick Royal Alb.	0-2	1-3	0-1	3-4	5-2	1-1	■	6-1	6-2	2-1	3-1	1-9	2-3
Heriot-Watt Univ.	1-1	0-2	1-1	2-2	3-1	0-2	0-1	■	3-1	3-5	0-6	2-2	1-2
Kelso United	3-2	2-3	2-2	1-1	3-4	1-0	0-1	3-2	■	2-4	2-5	3-5	2-5
Preston Athletic	1-1	0-1	1-1	1-0	4-0	1-1	3-3	0-2	2-0	■	3-0	1-0	1-1
Selkirk	2-3	1-2	1-4	0-3	2-1	3-2	2-1	0-5	1-1	2-2	■	2-6	2-2
Threave Rovers	0-3	3-4	1-3	2-0	7-1	3-2	6-0	1-0	2-1	5-2	6-2	■	0-1
Vale of Leithen	2-2	1-2	4-2	1-0	7-0	1-0	2-2	6-0	0-0	2-4	5-3	1-0	■

East of Scotland League

Premier Division Season 1998/99

Easthouses Lily	24	16	7	1	45	20	55
Vale of Leithen	24	15	5	4	65	34	50
Coldstream FC	24	13	7	4	54	29	46
Threave Rovers	24	14	3	7	73	39	45
Preston Athletic	24	12	8	4	51	29	44
Hawick Royal Albion	24	9	6	9	49	52	33
Edinburgh United	24	8	8	8	38	39	32
Gala Fairydean	24	9	4	11	37	33	31
Selkirk FC	24	7	4	13	45	65	25
Edinburgh Athletic	24	6	6	12	31	52	24
Heriot-Watt University	24	5	5	14	31	50	20
Kelso United	24	4	4	16	33	62	16
Eyemouth United	24	2	5	17	26	74	11

Promoted: Easthouses Lily and Vale of Leithen

(left) City Park,
home of The Spartans FC

(right) Meadowbank Stadium,
home of Edinburgh City FC

(left) Albert Park,
home of Hawick Royal Albert FC

(right) Netherdale,
home of Gala Fairydean FC

The following statistics were supplied by –

THE ASSOCIATION OF FOOTBALL STATISTICIANS
P.O. BOX 5828
BASILDON
ESSEX
SS15 5GQ

Telephone (01268) 416020
Fax   (01268) 543559

For further information about the AFS, please forward a 1st Class Stamp
to the above address together with your own name and address.

SCOTTISH LEAGUE CUP 1998/99

First Round

1st Aug 1998	Arbroath	0	Clydebank	1	
1st Aug 1998	Brechin City	2	Hamilton Academical	2	(aet)
Hamilton Academical won on penalties					
1st Aug 1998	Clyde	1	Berwick Rangers	1	(aet)
Berwick Rangers won on penalties					
1st Aug 1998	Cowdenbeath	0	Livingston	2	
1st Aug 1998	Dumbarton	0	Alloa Athletic	4	
1st Aug 1998	East Fife	3	Partick Thistle	2	(aet)
1st Aug 1998	Forfar Athletic	0	Stirling Albion	1	
1st Aug 1998	Queen of the South	1	Inverness Caled. Thistle	4	
1st Aug 1998	Queen's Park	1	Ayr United	3	
1st Aug 1998	Ross County	4	Montrose	1	
1st Aug 1998	Stenhousemuir	1	East Stirlingshire	0	
1st Aug 1998	Stranraer	1	Albion Rovers	1	(aet)
Stranraer won on penalties					

Second Round

8th Aug 1998	Berwick Rangers	1	Falkirk	5	
8th Aug 1998	Dundee	0	Alloa Athletic	1	
8th Aug 1998	Dundee United	2	Stirling Albion	2	(aet)
Dundee United won on penalties					
8th Aug 1998	East Fife	0	Motherwell	1	(aet)
8th Aug 1998	Greenock Morton	0	Ross County	1	
8th Aug 1998	Hamilton Academical	1	Hibernian	2	
8th Aug 1998	Livingston	1	Dunfermline Athletic	0	(aet)
8th Aug 1998	Raith Rovers	2	Clydebank	0	
8th Aug 1998	Stenhousemuir	0	Airdrieonians	2	
8th Aug 1998	St. Johnstone	3	Stranraer	0	
8th Aug 1998	St. Mirren	1	Ayr United	3	
8th Aug 1998	Inverness Caled. Thistle	0	Aberdeen	3	

Third Round

18th Aug 1998	Falkirk	0	St. Johnstone	1	
18th Aug 1998	Kilmarnock	3	Livingston	1	(aet)
18th Aug 1998	Rangers	4	Alloa Athletic	0	
19th Aug 1998	Airdrieonians	1	Celtic	0	

Third Round (Continued)

19th Aug 1998	Heart of Midlothian 4	Raith Rovers 2	(aet)
19th Aug 1998	Hibernian 1	Aberdeen 0	
18th Aug 1998	Motherwell 0	Ayr United 2	
19th Aug 1998	Ross County 2	Dundee United 0	(aet)

Quarter-Finals

8th Sep 1998	St. Johnstone 4	Hibernian 0	
8th Sep 1998	Ayr United 0	Rangers 2	
8th Sep 1998	Kilmarnock 0	Airdrieonians 1	(aet)
9th Sep 1998	Heart of Midlothian 1	Ross County 1	(aet)

Heart of Midlothian won on penalties

Semi-Finals

25th Oct 1998	Rangers 5	Airdrieonians 0
27th Oct 1998	St. Johnstone 3	Heart of Midlothian 0

FINAL

29th Nov 1998	Rangers 2	St. Johnstone 1

Guivarc'h 6, Albertz 37   Dasovic 8

Attendance: 45,533

Rangers: Niemi, Porrini, Amoruso, Hendry, Numan, B. Ferguson, Kanchelskis, Van Bronckhorst, Guivarc'h (Durie 89), Wallace, Albertz (I. Ferguson 65).

St. Johnstone: Main, McQuillan, Dasovic, Kernaghan, Scott, O'Neil, O'Boyle (Lowndes 74), Kane, Bollan, Dods, Simao (Grant 84).

SCOTTISH F.A. CUP 1998/99

First Round

5th Dec 1998	Arbroath	1	Partick Thistle	2
5th Dec 1998	Dumbarton	1	Livingston	1
5th Dec 1998	Queen's Park	2	Berwick Rangers	0
5th Dec 1998	Stenhousemuir	1	Alloa Athletic	1

Replays

12th Dec 1998	Alloa Athletic	0	Stenhousemuir	2
8th Dec 1998	Livingston	3	Dumbarton	0

Second Round

2nd Jan 1999	Civil Service Strollers	0	Albion Rovers	3
2nd Jan 1999	Dalbeattie Star	1	East Stirlingshire	2
2nd Jan 1999	Forfar Athletic	2	East Fife	2
2nd Jan 1999	Huntly	3	Peterhead	0
2nd Jan 1999	Inverness Caled. Thistle	1	Livingston	2
2nd Jan 1999	Keith	0	Brechin City	0
2nd Jan 1999	Montrose	0	Stirling Albion	0
2nd Jan 1999	Partick Thistle	5	Cowdenbeath	2
9th Jan 1999	Queen of the South	1	Ross County	3
18th Jan 1999	Queen's Park	1	Clachnacuddin	1
2nd Jan 1999	Spartans	1	Clyde	1
2nd Jan 1999	Whitehill Welfare	1	Stenhousemuir	1

Replays

9th Jan 1999	Brechin City	3	Keith	1
23rd Jan 1999	Clachnacuddin	2	Queen's Park	3
6th Jan 1999	Clyde	5	Spartans	0
9th Jan 1999	East Fife	0	Forfar Athletic	1
9th Jan 1999	Stenhousemuir	2	Whitehill Welfare	0
18th Jan 1999	Stirling Albion	2	Montrose	1

Third Round

23rd Jan 1999	Aberdeen	0	Livingston	1
23rd Jan 1999	Ayr United	3	Kilmarnock	0
23rd Jan 1999	Brechin City	1	Albion Rovers	1
23rd Jan 1999	Celtic	3	Airdrieonians	1
3rd Feb 1999	Clydebank	1	Ross County	1

Third Round (Continued)

23rd Jan 1999	Falkirk	3	Huntly	0
23rd Jan 1999	Hibernian	1	Stirling Albion	1
23rd Jan 1999	Greenock Morton	2	Dundee	1
24th Jan 1999	Motherwell	3	Heart of Midlothian	1
23rd Jan 1999	Partick Thistle	1	Dunfermline Athletic	2
2nd Feb 1999	Queen's Park	0	Dundee United	0
23rd Jan 1999	Raith Rovers	0	Clyde	4
23rd Jan 1999	Rangers	2	Stenhousemuir	0
23rd Jan 1999	St. Mirren	1	Hamilton Academical	1
23rd Jan 1999	St. Johnstone	1	Forfar Athletic	0
23rd Jan 1999	Stranraer	1	East Stirlingshire	0

Replays

2nd Feb 1999	Albion Rovers	3	Brechin City	1	
9th Feb 1999	Dundee United	1	Queen's Park	0	
2nd Feb 1999	Hamilton Academical	1	St. Mirren	0	
15th Feb 1999	Ross County	2	Clydebank	3	(aet)
2nd Feb 1999	Stirling Albion	2	Hibernian	1	

Fourth Round

13th Feb 1999	Ayr United	1	Albion Rovers	0
13th Feb 1999	Celtic	4	Dunfermline Athletic	0
3rd Mar 1999	Clydebank	2	Dundee United	2
14th Feb 1999	Hamilton Academical	0	Rangers	6
13th Feb 1999	Livingston	1	St. Johnstone	3
13th Feb 1999	Greenock Morton	6	Clyde	1
13th Feb 1999	Motherwell	2	Stirling Albion	0
13th Feb 1999	Stranraer	1	Falkirk	2

Replay

6th Mar 1999	Dundee United	3	Clydebank	0

Fifth Round

13th Mar 1999	Ayr United	0	Dundee United	0
8th Mar 1999	Greenock Morton	0	Celtic	3
6th Mar 1999	Motherwell	0	St. Johnstone	2
7th Mar 1999	Rangers	2	Falkirk	1

Fifth Round Replay

16th Mar 1999   Dundee United 2   Ayr United 1

Semi-Finals

10th Apr 1999   Celtic 2   Dundee United 0
11th Apr 1999   St. Johnstone 0   Rangers 4

FINAL

29th May 1999   Rangers 1   Celtic 0

Wallace 48

Attendance: 52,760

Rangers: Klos, Porrini (sub. Kanchelskis 77), Amoruso, Hendry, Vidmar, McCann (sub. I. Ferguson 67), McInnes, Van Bronckhorst, Wallace, Amato (sub. Wilson 90), Albertz.

Celtic: Gould, Boyd, Mahe (sub. O'Donnell 78), Stubbs, Larsson, Wieghorst, Lambert, Annoni (sub. Johnson 60), Blinker, Moravcik, Mjallby.

SCOTLAND INTERNATIONAL LINE-UPS AND STATISTICS 1998-99

5th September 1998
v LITHUANIA (ECQ) *Vilnius*

Leighton	Aberdeen
Elliott	Leicester City
Boyd	Celtic
Calderwood	Tott'ham Hotspur (sub. Davidson 72)
Hendry	Rangers
Dailly	Blackburn Rovers
Gallacher	Blackburn Rovers
Lambert	Celtic
McCoist	Kilmarnock (sub. McCann 84)
Jackson	Celtic (sub. B. Ferguson 58)
Collins	Everton

Result 0-0

31st March 1999
v CZECH REPUBLIC (ECQ) *Celtic Park*

Sullivan	Wimbledon
Weir	Heart of Midlothian
Boyd	Celtic
Lambert	Celtic
Elliott	Leicester City
Davidson	Blackburn Rovers (sub. Johnston 52)
Hopkin	Leeds United
Burley	Celtic
Jess	Aberdeen
McAllister	Coventry City (sub. Hutchison 64)
McCann	Rangers

Result 1-2 Jess

10th October 1998
ESTONIA (ECQ) *Edinburgh*

Leighton	Aberdeen
Weir	Heart of Midlothian
Boyd	Celtic
Calderwood	Tott'ham Hotspur (sub. Donnelly 57)
Hendry	Rangers
Davidson	Blackburn Rovers
Gallacher	Blackburn Rovers (sub. Jackson 18)
B. McKinlay	Blackburn Rovers
McCoist	Kilmarnock (sub. Dodds 69)
Durrant	Kilmarnock
Johnston	Sunderland

Result 3-2 Dodds 2, Hohlov-Simson (og)

28th April 1999
v GERMANY *Bremen*

Sullivan	Wimbledon
Weir	Heart of Midlothian
Hendry	Rangers (sub. Ritchie 66)
Boyd	Celtic
Gemmill	Nottm. Forest (sub. Jess 57)
Durrant	Kilmarnock (sub. Winters 72)
Lambert	Celtic (sub. Cameron 84)
A. Johnston	Sunderland (sub. B. O'Neil 86)
Davidson	Blackburn Rovers (sub. Whyte 79)
Hutchison	Everton
Dodds	Dundee

Result 1-0 Hutchison

14th October 1998
v FAROE ISLANDS (ECQ) *Aberdeen*

Sullivan	Wimbledon
Weir	Hearts (sub. Elliott)
Boyd	Celtic
Elliott	Leicester City
Hendry	Rangers
Davidson	Blackburn Rovers
B. McKinlay	Blackburn Rovers (sub. Durrant 46)
Burley	Celtic
Donnelly	Celtic
Dodds	Celtic
Johnston	Sunderland (sub. Glass 80)

Result 2-1 Burley, Dodds

5th June 1999
v FAROE ISLANDS (ECQ) *Toftir*

Sullivan	Wimbledon
Weir	Heart of Midlothian
Boyd	Celtic
Calderwood	Aston Villa
Elliott	Leicester City
Davidson	Blackburn Rovers
Dodds	Dundee
Lambert	Celtic
Gallacher	Blackburn Rovers (sub. Jess 89)
Durrant	Kilmarnock (sub. Cameron 46)
Johnston	Sunderland (sub. Gemmill 86)

Result 1-1 Johnston

9th June 1999
v CZECH REPUBLIC (ECQ) *Prague*

Sullivan	Wimbledon
Weir	Heart of Midlothian
Boyd	Celtic
Calderwood	Middlesbrough
Ritchie	Heart of Midlothian
Davidson	Blackburn Rovers
Dodds	Dundee
Lambert	Celtic
Gallacher	Blackburn Rovers
Durrant	Kilmarnock (sub. Jess 71)
Johnston	Sunderland

Result 2-3 Ritchie, Johnston

Our publication : –

SCOTLAND INTERNATIONAL LINE-UPS AND STATISTICS 1872-1960

is now available priced £5.95 per copy post free from : –

Soccer Books Limited
72 St. Peter's Avenue
Cleethorpes
N.E. Lincolnshire
DN35 8HU

Also available late 1999 (same price): –

SCOTLAND INTERNATIONAL LINE-UPS AND STATISTICS 1961-1999

THE 25 YEAR RECORD SERIES

Top quality 25 Season histories with line-ups, results, scorers, attendances and season-by-season write-ups.

Titles currently available:

Manchester United *(Priced £5.99)* ..... Seasons 1974-75 to 1998-99

Hearts .... Seasons 1973-74 to 1997-98
Manchester City F.C. .... Seasons 1973-74 to 1997-98
Watford F.C. .... Seasons 1973-74 to 1997-98
West Ham United F.C. .... Seasons 1973-74 to 1997-98

Arsenal F.C. .... Seasons 1972-73 to 1996-97
Crystal Palace F.C. .... Seasons 1972-73 to 1996-97
Spurs .... Seasons 1972-73 to 1996-97
West Bromwich Albion F.C. .... Seasons 1972-73 to 1996-97
Wolves .... Seasons 1972-73 to 1996-97

Aberdeen F.C. .... Seasons 1971-72 to 1995-96
Chelsea F.C. .... Seasons 1971-72 to 1995-96
Middlesbrough F.C. .... Seasons 1971-72 to 1995-96
Preston North End F.C. .... Seasons 1971-72 to 1995-96
Southampton F.C. .... Seasons 1971-72 to 1995-96
Sunderland F.C. .... Seasons 1971-72 to 1995-96

Celtic F.C. .... Seasons 1970-71 to 1994-95
Derby County F.C. .... Seasons 1970-71 to 1994-95
Everton F.C. .... Seasons 1970-71 to 1994-95
Leeds United F.C. .... Seasons 1970-71 to 1994-95
Liverpool F.C. .... Seasons 1970-71 to 1994-95
Newcastle United F.C. .... Seasons 1970-71 to 1994-95
Rangers F.C. .... Seasons 1970-71 to 1994-95

Also available (no write-ups):

Burnley F.C. .... Seasons 1969-70 to 1993-94

All titles are softback and priced £4.99 (except Manchester Utd.)

Available post free from:

Soccer Books Limited (Dept. SBL)
72 St. Peter's Avenue
Cleethorpes   Tel: (01472) 696226
N.E. Lincolnshire   Fax: (01472) 698546
DN35 8HU